The
Anatomy Student's
REVISION
WORKBOOK

Volume One

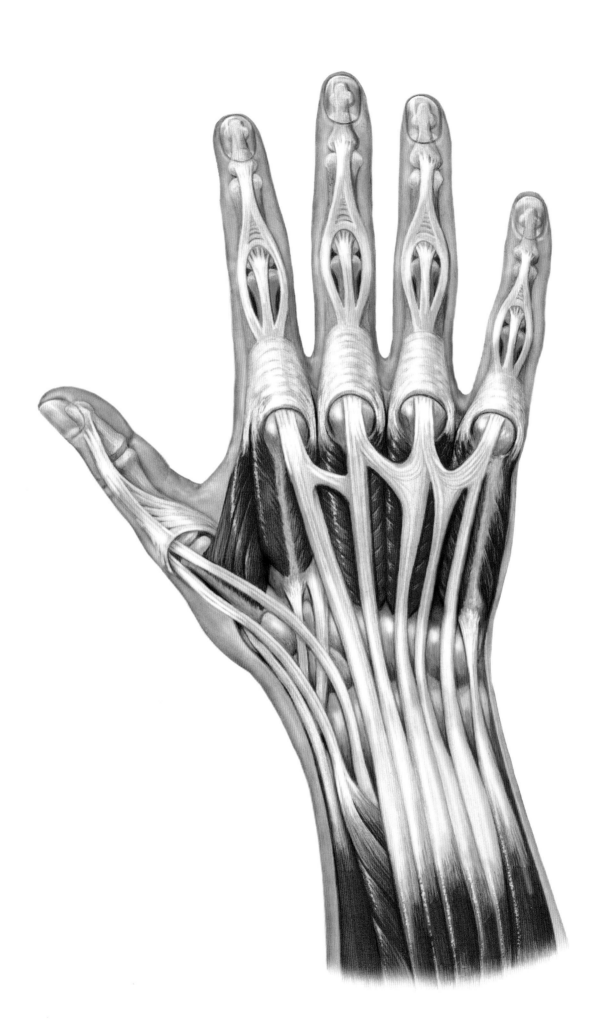

The Anatomy Student's REVISION WORKBOOK

Volume One

Professor Ken Ashwell BMedSc, MBBS, PhD

QUAD BOOKS

Inspiring | Educating | Creating | Entertaining

Brimming with creative inspiration, how-to projects, and useful information to enrich your everyday life, Quarto Knows is a favourite destination for those pursuing their interests and passions. Visit our site and dig deeper with our books into your area of interest: Quarto Creates, Quarto Cooks, Quarto Homes, Quarto Lives, Quarto Drives, Quarto Explores, Quarto Gifts, or Quarto Kids.

© 2018 Quarto Publishing plc

Conceived, Designed and Produced by Quad Books, an imprint of The Quarto Group
The Old Brewery, 6 Blundell Street, London N7 9BH, United Kingdom
T (0)20 7700 6700 **F** (0)20 7700 8066 **www.QuartoKnows.com**

ISBN: 978-0-85762-593-9

Design: Tony Seddon

Illustrations: © Global Publishing Pty Ltd

Printed and Bound in China

Contents

8   How this book works

10   Chapter 1: Body Systems and Tissues
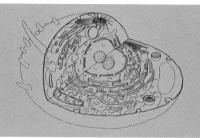

36   Chapter 2: The Musculoskeletal System
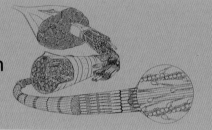

78   Chapter 3: The Nervous System
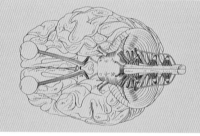

120   Chapter 4: The Circulatory System

158   Chapter 5: The Respiratory System
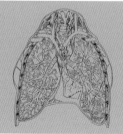

184   Answers

189   Index

How this book works

Anatomy is a complex subject that incorporates not only visual knowledge – such as the recognition of body features, their shapes and positions – but also declarative or factual information about the structure and function of body parts. Once a student has reviewed lecture and practical class material, it is time to test that knowledge against well-crafted questions that can reveal weaknesses and focus attention on specific topics for further revision. It is only by repeated sequences of knowledge testing and review of educational material that a student can progress towards a sound understanding of the field.

This compact yet detailed book combines the testing of visual recognition through comprehensive labelling tasks, with the assessment of factual knowledge through multiple choice, true or false, and sentence completion exercises. It also tests deeper understanding of the reasoning behind structure/function relationships in anatomy through the use of matching-statement-to-reason exercises.

Topics in this book are ordered by body system, with useful summaries and concise definitions of key terms and concepts. Understanding of the clinical relevance of the content is reinforced by the provision of focused, informative text boxes for each system, so that readers can appreciate the practical importance of the information.

Full answers to all questions are included on pages 184–188.

Summary pages

A brief summary of the broad topic, and labelled, full-colour illustrations, are combined with definitions of the key terms.

Definitions
Arranged in alphabetical order, concise entries define the body parts labelled on the illustrations on the facing page. Each term in bold corresponds to a label.

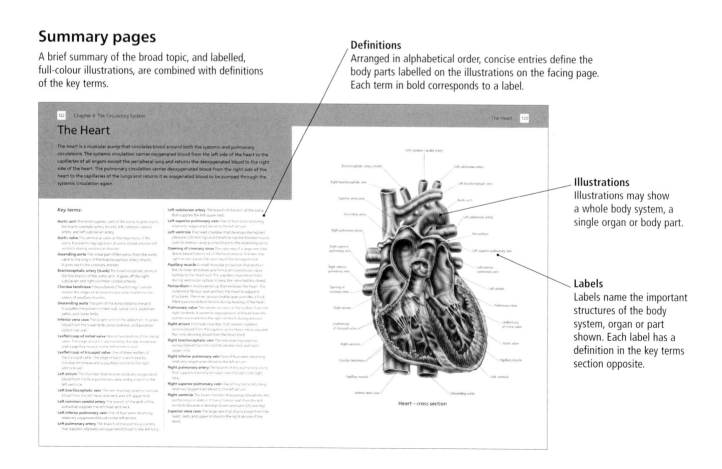

Illustrations
Illustrations may show a whole body system, a single organ or body part.

Labels
Labels name the important structures of the body system, organ or part shown. Each label has a definition in the key terms section opposite.

Exercise pages

Exercises include true-or-false questions, multiple-choice questions, filling the blanks, and matching statements to the correct reasons. Instructions are given on each page, and full answers are included on pages 184–188.

Chapter name

Subsection

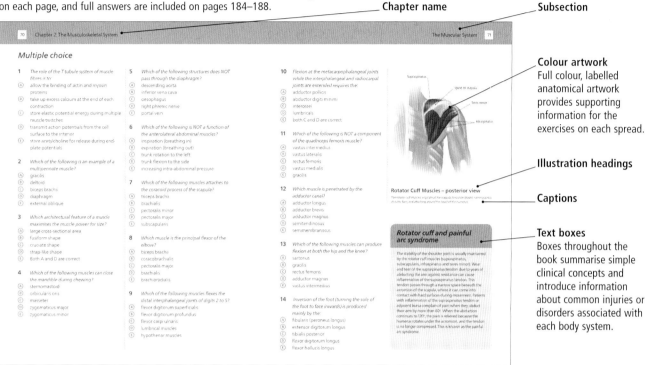

Colour artwork
Full colour, labelled anatomical artwork provides supporting information for the exercises on each spread.

Illustration headings

Captions

Text boxes
Boxes throughout the book summarise simple clinical concepts and introduce information about common injuries or disorders associated with each body system.

Colour and label pages

Featuring different colour-and-label activities to help you to identify and memorise the location of different body parts.

Blank labels
Numbered blank labels refer to body parts. Fill in the labels to test your anatomical knowledge.

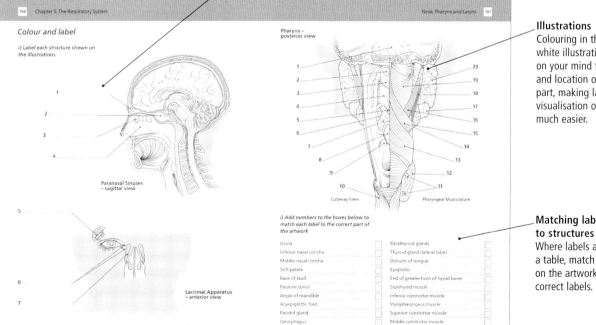

Illustrations
Colouring in the black-and-white illustrations imprints on your mind the shape and location of each body part, making later visualisation of the parts much easier.

Matching labels to structures
Where labels are given in a table, match the numbers on the artwork to the correct labels.

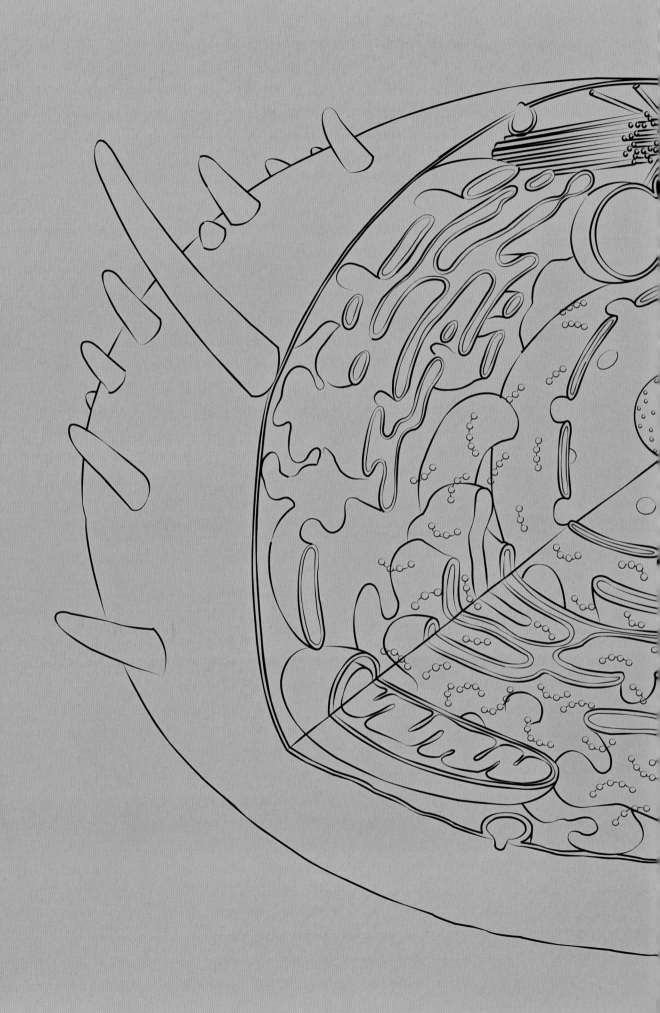

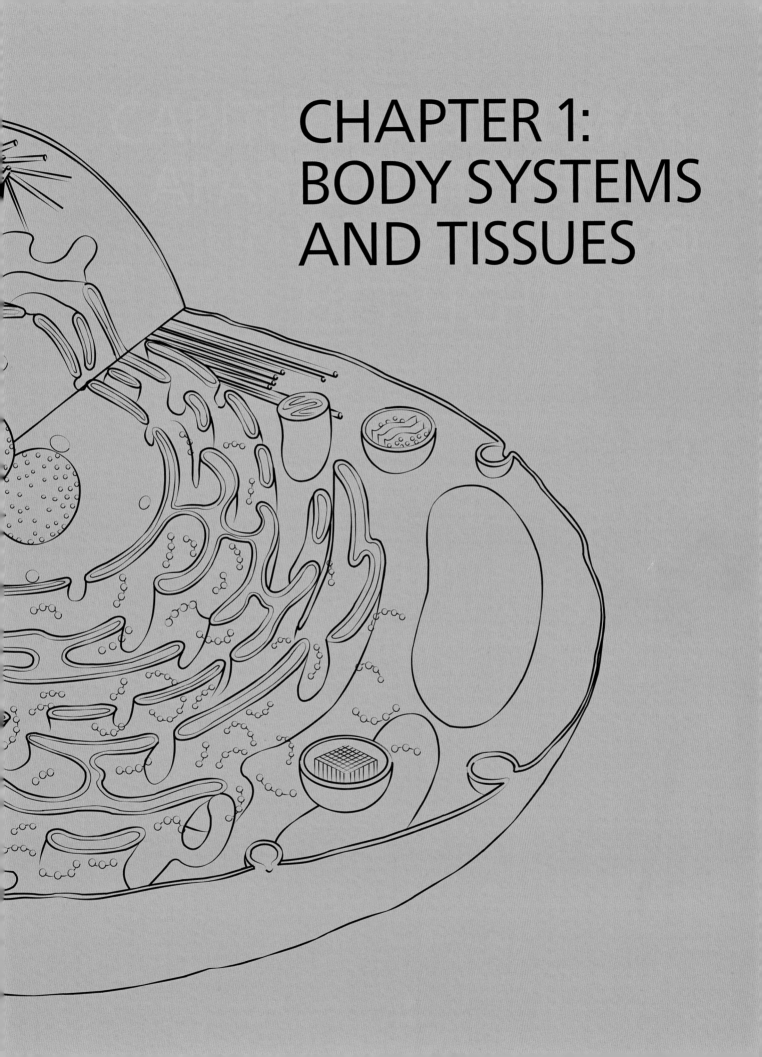

CHAPTER 1:
BODY SYSTEMS
AND TISSUES

Body Systems Overview

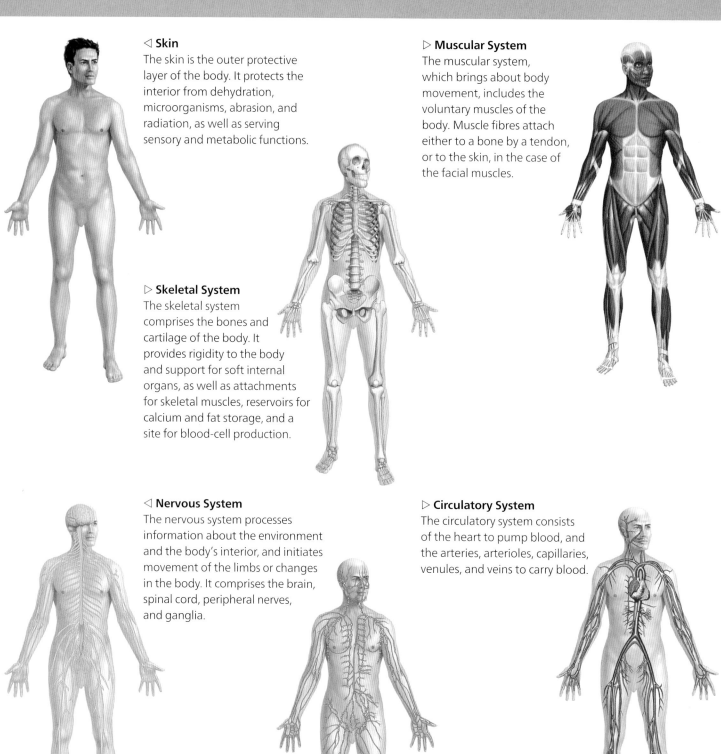

◁ **Skin**

The skin is the outer protective layer of the body. It protects the interior from dehydration, microorganisms, abrasion, and radiation, as well as serving sensory and metabolic functions.

▷ **Muscular System**

The muscular system, which brings about body movement, includes the voluntary muscles of the body. Muscle fibres attach either to a bone by a tendon, or to the skin, in the case of the facial muscles.

▷ **Skeletal System**

The skeletal system comprises the bones and cartilage of the body. It provides rigidity to the body and support for soft internal organs, as well as attachments for skeletal muscles, reservoirs for calcium and fat storage, and a site for blood-cell production.

◁ **Nervous System**

The nervous system processes information about the environment and the body's interior, and initiates movement of the limbs or changes in the body. It comprises the brain, spinal cord, peripheral nerves, and ganglia.

▷ **Circulatory System**

The circulatory system consists of the heart to pump blood, and the arteries, arterioles, capillaries, venules, and veins to carry blood.

▷ **Lymphatic System**

The lymphatic system comprises a series of delicate channels that drain tissue fluid through lymph nodes. It contains lymphocytes and macrophages to sweep up foreign proteins, microbes, and cancer cells.

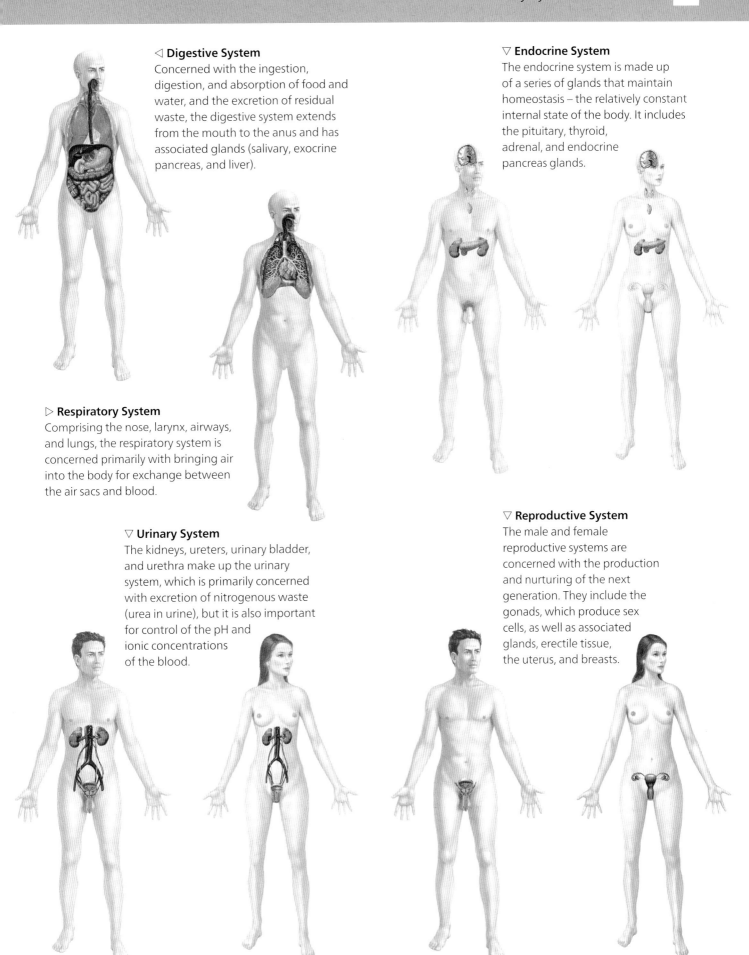

◁ Digestive System

Concerned with the ingestion, digestion, and absorption of food and water, and the excretion of residual waste, the digestive system extends from the mouth to the anus and has associated glands (salivary, exocrine pancreas, and liver).

▷ Respiratory System

Comprising the nose, larynx, airways, and lungs, the respiratory system is concerned primarily with bringing air into the body for exchange between the air sacs and blood.

▽ Urinary System

The kidneys, ureters, urinary bladder, and urethra make up the urinary system, which is primarily concerned with excretion of nitrogenous waste (urea in urine), but it is also important for control of the pH and ionic concentrations of the blood.

▽ Endocrine System

The endocrine system is made up of a series of glands that maintain homeostasis – the relatively constant internal state of the body. It includes the pituitary, thyroid, adrenal, and endocrine pancreas glands.

▽ Reproductive System

The male and female reproductive systems are concerned with the production and nurturing of the next generation. They include the gonads, which produce sex cells, as well as associated glands, erectile tissue, the uterus, and breasts.

Body Regions

Key terms:

Abdomen (abdominal) The region of the trunk below the chest and above the pelvis. Abdominal: relating to the abdomen.

Ankle/Tarsus (tarsal) The junction of the leg and foot. Tarsal: relating to the ankle or proximal foot.

Arm/Brachium (brachial) The proximal part of the upper limb, consisting of the humerus and surrounding muscles, fascia (connective tissue), nerves, and vessels. Brachial: relating to the arm.

Armpit/Axilla (axillary) The hollow space at the base of the upper limb, situated between the arm, chest wall, and scapula. Axillary: relating to the armpit.

Big toe/Hallux Digit 1 of the foot.

Cheek (buccal) Usually refers to the facial region over the maxilla and zygomatic bone, but also extends to the lateral wall of the mouth. Buccal: relating to the cheek.

Chest/Thorax (thoracic) The part of the body bounded by the 12 ribs and the sternum. Thoracic: relating to the chest.

Chin (mental) The pointed inferior part of the mandible. Mental: relating to the chin.

Ear (otic) The external ear, pinna, or auricle; or more correctly used for the external, middle, and inner parts of the hearing apparatus. Otic: relating to the ear.

Elbow (antecubital) The junction of the arm and forearm. The antecubital region is the depression (cubital fossa) anterior to the elbow joint.

Eye (ocular or orbital) The organ of sight. The eye and associated glands, muscles, vessels, and nerves lie within the bony orbital cavity. Ocular: relating to the eye itself. Orbital: relating to the bony orbit.

Face (facial) The front of the head. The facial skeleton is covered by facial muscles and highly sensitive skin. Facial: relating to the face.

Fingers/Digits (digital or phalangeal) Digits of the hand. They have phalangeal bones as their core (two in the thumb or digit 1; three in digits 2–5). Digital: relating to fingers or toes. Phalangeal: relating to the phalangeal bones.

Foot/Pes (pedal) The terminal part of the lower limb. The foot consists of tarsal, metatarsal, and phalangeal bones, associated muscles, tendons, ligaments, vessels, and nerves. Pedal: relating to structures in the foot.

Forearm/Antebrachium (antebrachial) The part of the upper limb between the elbow and wrist. Antebrachial: relating to some constituents (e.g. nerves) of the forearm.

Forehead (frontal) The part of the face over the frontal bones of the skull. It has a thin layer of muscle (frontalis) beneath the skin. Frontal: relating to the forehead.

Groin/Inguen (inguinal) The area at the junction of the lower limb and the anterior abdominal wall. Inguinal: relating to the groin region.

Hand The distal extremity of the upper limb. It consists of the metacarpal bones (palm), phalangeal bones (digits), and associated muscles, tendons, vessels, and nerves.

Head The face and braincase. It contains major sensory organs as well as the entrances to the respiratory and gastrointestinal tracts.

Kneecap/Patella (patellar) The prominence of the knee. It is produced by the patella, a sesamoid bone in the tendon of the quadriceps femoris muscle. Patellar: relating to the kneecap.

Leg/Crus (crural) The part of the lower limb between the knee and ankle. Crural: relating to structures in the region.

Mouth (oral) The opening in the face bounded above by the hard and soft palate, below by the tongue, and on each side by the cheek (buccal wall). Oral: relating to the mouth.

Neck (cervical) The part of the body that connects the head and the trunk. Its core is the cervical vertebrae, which are surrounded by muscles, vessels, and nerves. Cervical: relating to the neck.

Nose (nasal) A protuberance on the face, formed from cartilage and bone, that houses the entrance to the nasal cavity. Nasal: relating to the nose.

Palm (palmar) The proximal part of the hand. Formed of the metacarpal bones and associated muscles, tendons, vessels, and nerves. Palmar: relating to the palm.

Pelvis (pelvic) Part of the skeleton formed by two hip bones on each side and the sacrum and coccyx in the midline.

Pubis (pubic) The pubic region at the front of the bony pelvis. Its contents include the pubic part of the hip bone and overlying tissues. Pubic: relating to the pubis.

Skull/Cranium (cranial) Consists of the facial skeleton and the braincase (calvaria). It protects the brain. Cranial: relating to the cranium.

Thigh (femoral) The region of the proximal lower limb that has the femur at its core with the quadriceps femoris muscle anteriorly and hamstring and adductor muscles posteriorly and medially. Femoral: relating to the thigh.

Thumb/Pollex (pollical) Digit 1 of the hand. Pollical: relating to the thumb.

Toes/Digits (digital or phalangeal) Digits (1–5) of the lower limb. They contain phalangeal bones. Digital: relating to the toes or fingers. Phalangeal: relating to the phalanges.

Trunk/Torso Comprises the thoracic and abdominopelvic cavities and their musculoskeletal walls.

Umbilicus (umbilical) A puckered scar where the umbilical cord was attached during prenatal life. Umbilical: relating to the umbilicus.

Wrist (carpal) Comprises the carpal bones and tendons transmitting muscle power from the forearm to the fingers. Carpal: relating to the wrist.

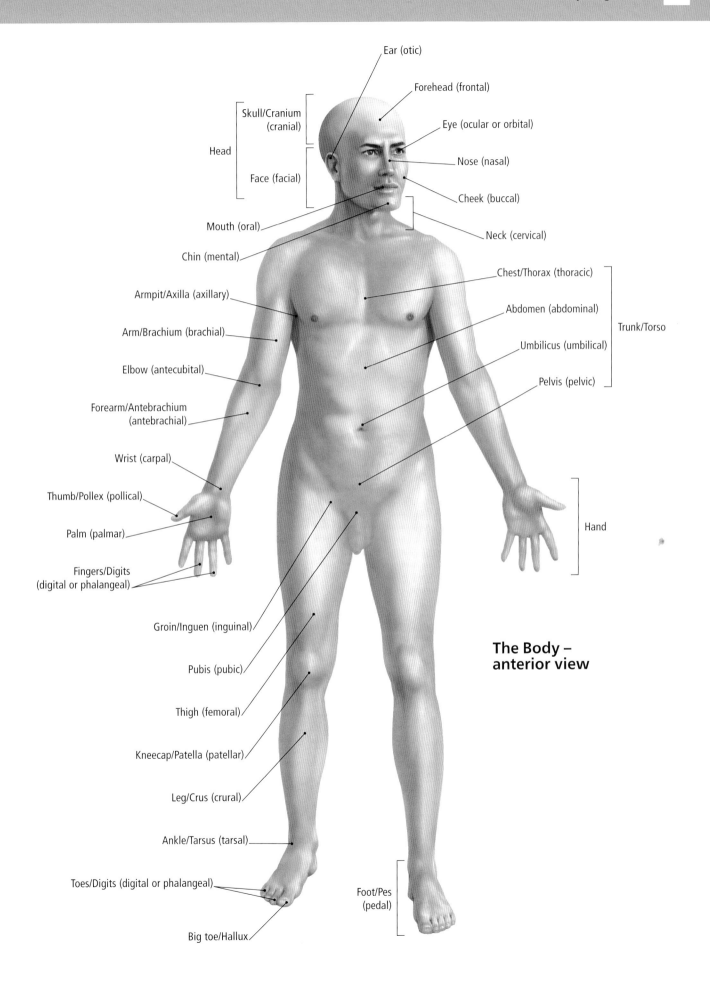

Ear (otic)

Forehead (frontal)

Skull/Cranium
(cranial)

Eye (ocular or orbital)

Head

Nose (nasal)

Face (facial)

Cheek (buccal)

Mouth (oral)

Neck (cervical)

Chin (mental)

Chest/Thorax (thoracic)

Armpit/Axilla (axillary)

Abdomen (abdominal)

Trunk/Torso

Arm/Brachium (brachial)

Umbilicus (umbilical)

Elbow (antecubital)

Pelvis (pelvic)

Forearm/Antebrachium
(antebrachial)

Wrist (carpal)

Thumb/Pollex (pollical)

Hand

Palm (palmar)

Fingers/Digits
(digital or phalangeal)

Groin/Inguen (inguinal)

**The Body –
anterior view**

Pubis (pubic)

Thigh (femoral)

Kneecap/Patella (patellar)

Leg/Crus (crural)

Ankle/Tarsus (tarsal)

Toes/Digits (digital or phalangeal)

Foot/Pes
(pedal)

Big toe/Hallux

Body Regions

Key terms:

Abdominal cavity The upper part of the abdominopelvic cavity, containing the stomach, intestines, liver, kidneys, and pancreas.

Abdominopelvic cavity The largest ventral cavity of the body, extending from the diaphragm above to the pelvic floor muscles below.

Back (dorsal) The posterior or dorsal part of the body, including the vertebral column and associated muscles.

Buttock/Gluteus (gluteal) The fleshy part of the body posterior to the pelvis and upper femur, composed of gluteal muscles and fat. Gluteal: relating to the buttock.

Calf/Sura (sural) The fleshy part of the posterior leg, largely composed of the triceps surae muscle. Sural: relating to the calf.

Cranial cavity The interior of the skull or cranium. It houses the brain, pituitary gland, and associated blood vessels.

Diaphragm A sheet of muscle and tendon separating the thoracic and abdominal cavities. It is perforated by the aorta, inferior vena cava, and oesophagus.

Dorsal cavity The body cavity containing the brain, spinal cord, and their membranes (meninges).

Elbow/Olecranon (olecranal) The elbow is the junction of the arm and forearm. The posterior aspect of the elbow is marked by a bony projection called the olecranon. Olecranal: relating to the olecranon.

Head See pp. 14–15.

Heel/Calcaneus (calcaneal) The core of the heel is the calcaneus bone. Calcaneal: relating to some structures in this region.

Lower back (lumbar) The region of the body that has the lumbar vertebrae and flanking muscles at its core. Lumbar: relating to the lower back.

Lower limb Consists of the thigh (femoral region), leg (crus), foot (pes), and digits.

Mediastinum The space in the chest between the two pleural sacs and their enclosed lungs. It contains the heart, major vessels, and oesophagus.

Neck (cervical) See pp. 14–15.

Pelvic cavity The space bounded by the hip bones, sacrum, coccyx, and pelvic diaphragm. It contains the urinary bladder, reproductive organs, rectum, and anus.

Pericardial cavity The sac that lies in the mediastinum of the thorax and encloses the heart. It contains a fluid space to allow free movement of the beating heart.

Shoulder (acromial) The junction of the clavicle, scapula, and humerus. Its rounded shape is produced by the deltoid muscle, arising from the spine and acromial process of the scapula and distal clavicle, and covering the head of the humerus. Acromial: relating to the shoulder.

Sole (plantar) The inferior or plantar surface of the foot. Plantar: relating to the sole.

Spinal canal A hollow cavity that extends the length of the vertebral column. It contains the spinal cord and cauda equina.

Thoracic cavity The upper ventral cavity of the trunk. It is divided into paired pleural sacs enclosing the lungs, and the mediastinum in the midline.

Trunk/Torso See pp. 14–15.

Upper limb Comprises the arm (brachium), forearm (antebrachium), hand (manus), and digits.

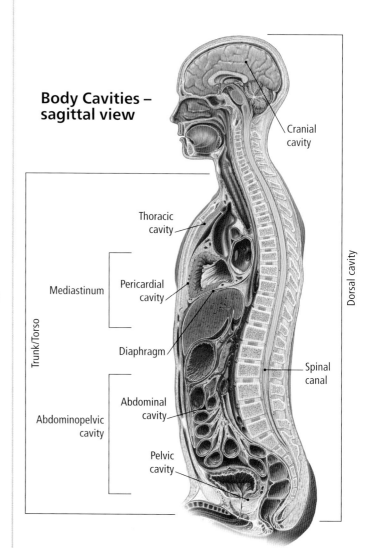

Body Cavities – sagittal view

Cranial cavity

Thoracic cavity

Mediastinum

Pericardial cavity

Trunk/Torso

Diaphragm

Dorsal cavity

Spinal canal

Abdominal cavity

Abdominopelvic cavity

Pelvic cavity

**The Body –
posterior view**

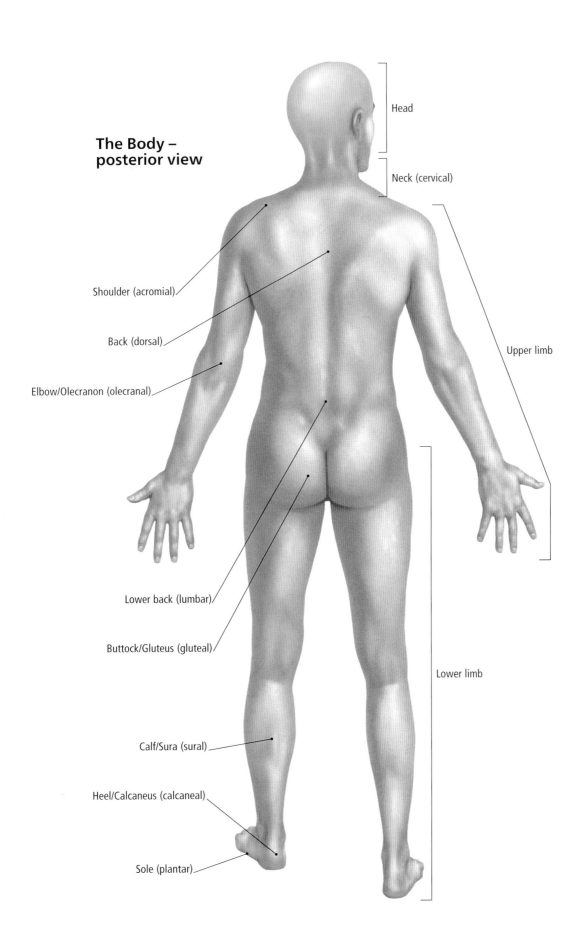

Head

Neck (cervical)

Shoulder (acromial)

Back (dorsal)

Elbow/Olecranon (olecranal)

Upper limb

Lower back (lumbar)

Buttock/Gluteus (gluteal)

Lower limb

Calf/Sura (sural)

Heel/Calcaneus (calcaneal)

Sole (plantar)

View Orientation and Anatomical Planes

The study of anatomy requires clear communication, and that is facilitated by the use of a standard body arrangement and agreed descriptive terms. The anatomical position is a standard body position that must be used when describing the location of body parts. In the anatomical position, the subject stands with the two feet together and facing forwards. The two hands are by the side with the palms facing the front and the thumb to the lateral side. The head is erect, and the eyes look forwards.

Key terms:

Anterior Toward the front of the body.

Distal Toward the end of an extremity.

Dorsal Toward the back of the body in the trunk, but superiorly in the head. The difference is due to the fact that the dorsum is defined relative to the axis of the nervous system, which bends at the midbrain in humans.

Dorsal surface (of foot or hand) The top of the foot or back of the hand.

Frontal (coronal) plane The anatomical plane that divides the body into front and back parts.

Inferior Toward the feet or downward.

Lateral Toward the side of the body.

Medial Toward the midline of the body.

Palmar surface The anterior surface (palm) of the hand.

Plantar surface The inferior surface (sole) of the foot.

Posterior Toward the back of the body.

Proximal Toward the attachment of a limb to the trunk, or toward the beginning of a tubular structure.

Sagittal plane A family of planes that divide the body into left and right parts. One of the planes is in the midline (mid-sagittal or median) and divides the body into two equal halves. The remaining members of the family (para-sagittal or para-median) divide the body into unequal left and right parts.

Sagittal (mid-sagittal or median) plane The plane that divides the body into two equal halves.

Sagittal (para-sagittal or para-median) plane One of a family of planes parallel to the midline.

Superior Toward the upper end of the body.

Transverse (axial) plane The family of planes that divide the body into upper and lower parts.

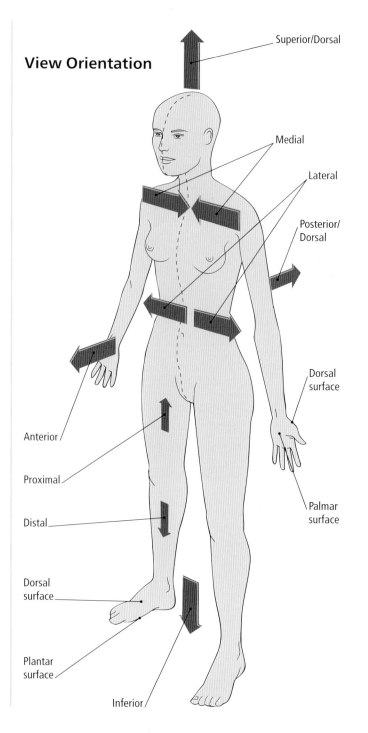

View Orientation

Superior/Dorsal
Medial
Lateral
Posterior/Dorsal
Dorsal surface
Palmar surface
Anterior
Proximal
Distal
Dorsal surface
Plantar surface
Inferior

Anatomical Planes

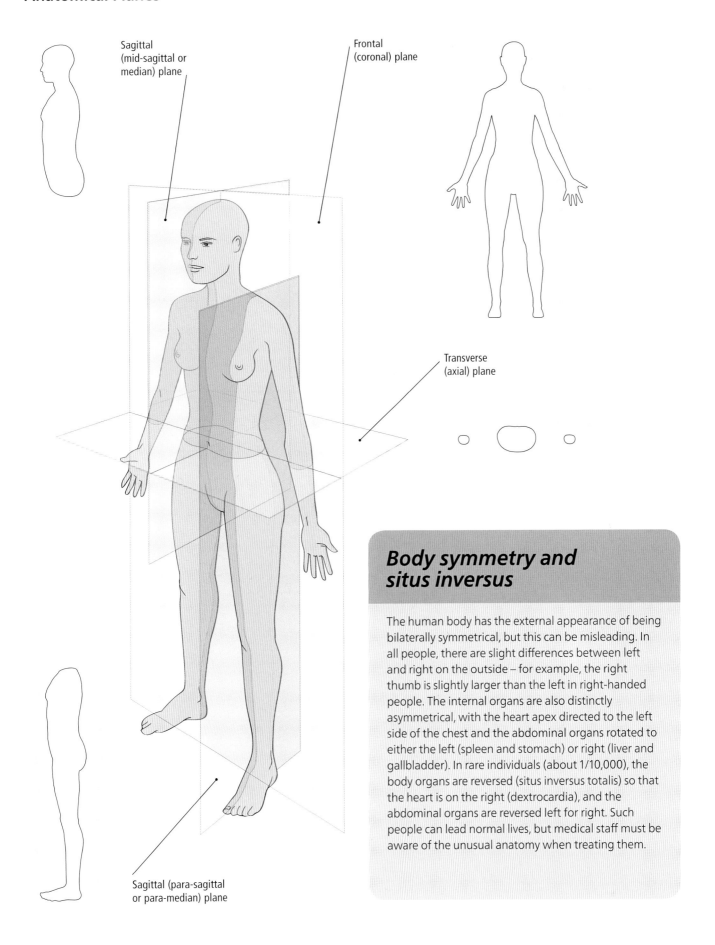

Sagittal (mid-sagittal or median) plane

Frontal (coronal) plane

Transverse (axial) plane

Sagittal (para-sagittal or para-median) plane

Body symmetry and situs inversus

The human body has the external appearance of being bilaterally symmetrical, but this can be misleading. In all people, there are slight differences between left and right on the outside – for example, the right thumb is slightly larger than the left in right-handed people. The internal organs are also distinctly asymmetrical, with the heart apex directed to the left side of the chest and the abdominal organs rotated to either the left (spleen and stomach) or right (liver and gallbladder). In rare individuals (about 1/10,000), the body organs are reversed (situs inversus totalis) so that the heart is on the right (dextrocardia), and the abdominal organs are reversed left for right. Such people can lead normal lives, but medical staff must be aware of the unusual anatomy when treating them.

Tissues

◁ **Collagen**
This structural protein makes up the bulk of connective tissue. Five different types are recognised. All collagen contains the amino acids hydroxyproline and hydroxylysine, which require vitamin C for their manufacture.

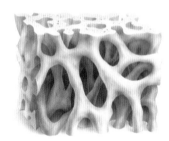

◁ **Bone Tissue**
A composite material comprising cells (osteocytes) in an extracellular matrix (collagen and mineral salts), bone acts as a structural material, as well as a store of calcium and phosphorus.

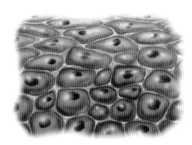

◁ **Epithelial Tissue**
Epithelial tissue comprises the surface cells of the body exterior (epidermis), as well as the linings and glands of the digestive, respiratory, and genito-urinary tracts. Epithelial cells may be flat (squamous), cuboidal, or columnar and may have specialised features on their apical cell surface to facilitate absorption or movement of mucus.

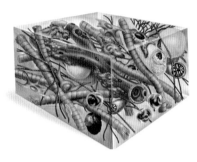

◁ **Loose Connective Tissue**
This connective tissue is made up of fibres arranged obliquely to each other. It has minimal structural strength, and its main role is to fill the spaces between organs.

◁ **Dense Connective Tissue**
Dense connective tissue is designed to withstand high tensile force. Strength is achieved by multiple, parallel arrays of collagen fibres. Examples include ligaments and tendons.

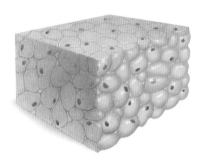

◁ **Adipose Tissue**
This fat tissue includes yellow fat, which is found under the skin in adults and stores energy, and brown fat, which has many mitochondria and is found on the upper back in newborn infants. Brown fat generates heat for thermoregulation.

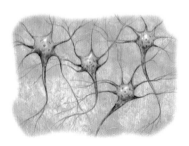

◁ **Neural Tissue**
Comprising nerve cells (neurons) and their supporting cells, neural tissue is concerned with the processing of sensory information and the rapid control of the body's systems.

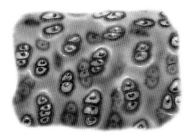

◁ **Cartilage Tissue: Hyaline Cartilage**
Found on the surfaces of synovial joints, hyaline cartilage has the ability to withstand cycles of compression and relaxation as the joint moves. During these cycles, synovial fluid is exchanged between the hyaline cartilage and the joint space.

◁ **Muscle Tissue: Smooth Muscle**
This non-striated involuntary muscle is found in the walls of the respiratory, gastro-intestinal, and genito-urinary tracts, as well as blood vessels.

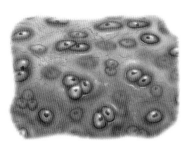

◁ **Cartilage Tissue: Elastic Cartilage**
Found in parts of the body where flexibility and elasticity are required, such as in the external ear (pinna or auricle), this is a type of cartilage with a high content of elastic fibres.

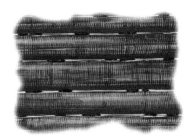

◁ **Muscle Tissue: Skeletal Muscle**
A type of voluntary striated (striped) muscle, usually with at least one attachment to the skeleton, skeletal muscle produces all voluntary movements either by contraction or by controlled relaxation.

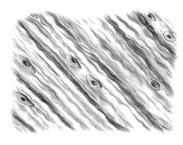

◁ **Cartilage Tissue: Fibrocartilage**
Found in parts of the body subjected to high compressive forces, such as the edges of intervertebral discs, fibrocartilage has a high content of fibrous tissue (that is, collagen fibres).

◁ **Muscle Tissue: Cardiac Muscle**
Cardiac muscle is a type of involuntary striated (striped) muscle tissue, and is found solely within the walls of the heart chambers. It is activated by the conducting and pace-making tissues within the heart, and is under the influence of the autonomic nervous system.

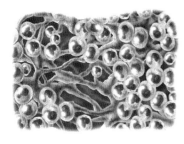

◁ **Immune System Tissue**
Concerned with the drainage of excess tissue fluid from the extracellular space and the immune surveillance of that fluid for microorganisms and cancer cells, immune system tissue consists of lymphatic vessels. These vessels drain through clusters of lymphoid (immune system) cells known as lymph nodes.

True or false?

1   *The median plane divides the body into two roughly equal halves.*   T

2   *A plane through the waistline would be a horizontal or transverse plane.*   T

DIAPHRAGM

3   *The mediastinum is the muscular structure that separates the thoracic and abdominal cavities.*   F

4   *The ventral body cavity can be further divided into thoracic, abdominal and pelvic cavities.*   T

5   *The ventral body cavity is continuous from the neck to the pelvic outlet.*

6   *The dorsal body cavity contains the heart and lungs.*   CNS   F

7   *The lymphatic system is mainly made up of immune system cells aggregated into large internal organs.*   F

Afferent lymphatic vessels

Follicle of cortex

Trabecula

Capsule

Capillary

Vein

Artery

Efferent lymphatic vessel

8   *Homeostasis is the ability of the body to maintain a relatively constant internal state.*   T

9   *Both the nervous and endocrine systems are involved with communication within the body.*   T

10   *The region of the cell that contains the genetic material (DNA) is the centriole.*   F

nucleus

Lymph Node

Clustered along the route of the lymphatic vessels, the lymph nodes filter and clean incoming lymph supplied through afferent vessels. Once filtered, efferent vessels carry the lymph to the venous system.

11	*The nucleolus is found in the ~~periphery of the cell body~~.* Nucleus	F
12	*Lysosomes contain enzymes that break down waste material, viruses and bacteria, and cellular debris.*	T
13	*Bone is a composite material of the mineral calcium carbonate and the protein collagen.*	F
14	*The ends of long bones are usually covered with a layer of ~~elastic~~ cartilage.* hyaline	F
15	*Cilia are motile extensions of the cell surface that are responsible for moving mucus and debris.*	T
16	*The tubular structure of long bones allows ~~minimal~~ strength for a given weight.* Maximal	F
17	*Smooth muscle cells are concentrated in the outer membranes of long bones.*	F
18	*The nervous system is concerned primarily with control of body changes over periods of days to months.*	F Quicker than that.
19	*Gut movement is mainly due to the actions of smooth muscle.*	T
20	*Glands of the gut are derived from the epithelial tissue.*	T

Defects in cilia function

Cilia are cellular organelles that beat rhythmically either to move the cell through fluid (such as in paramecia), or to waft fluid past cells (as in the human respiratory epithelium). Kartagener syndrome is a rare genetic condition that leads to defective function of cilia in the respiratory tract and the uterine tube, and defective flagella of sperm. Affected individuals experience recurrent respiratory tract infections, middle ear infections and sinusitis. In both sexes, there would be reduced fertility, because sperm cannot swim, and the uterine tube epithelium cannot move the egg.

Multiple choice

1 *The roles of the respiratory system include all of the following EXCEPT:*
(A) gas exchange
(B) thermoregulation
(C) pH regulation
(D) communication
(E) excretion of uric acid

2 *The urinary system includes all of the following organs EXCEPT:*
(A) kidney
(B) seminal vesicle
(C) urinary bladder
(D) ureter
(E) urethra

3 *Which of the following structures would be found in the ventral body cavity?*
(A) brain
(B) spinal cord
(C) pineal gland
(D) spleen
(E) pituitary gland

4 *Which direction in the body is defined with respect to the nervous system axis and is directed towards the back of the body in the trunk, but superiorly in the head?*
(A) anterior
(B) ventral
(C) posterior
(D) caudal
(E) dorsal

5 *A plane that passes through the two eyes and the pubic region would belong to which group?*
(A) parasagittal
(B) median
(C) frontal or coronal
(D) horizontal or transverse
(E) oblique

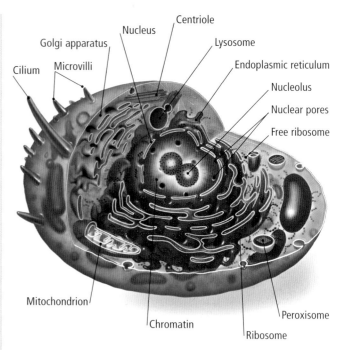

Cell Structure

Cells are the fundamental units of all living things. The human body contains trillions of cells, each containing our unique identity, our DNA.

6 *Which of the following cellular organelles is responsible for the production of protein?*
(A) nucleus
(B) nucleolus
(C) centriole
(D) ribosome
(E) mitochondrion

7 *Which structure would be found within the nucleus?*
(A) ribosome
(B) nucleolus
(C) mitochondrion
(D) microvillus
(E) Golgi apparatus

8   *The role of microvilli is to:*
(A)   increase cellular surface area for absorption
(B)   allow the cell to move freely in the body
(C)   transmit nuclear material between adjacent cells
(D)   allow cells to bind together to form tissue layers
(E)   provide a surface for energy production by metabolising glucose

9   *The role of the Golgi apparatus is to:*
(A)   store and retrieve genetic information to control cellular activities
(B)   produce lipids and proteins
(C)   package protein and lipid for transport and secretion
(D)   transmit information around the cell body
(E)   produce energy in the form of adenosine triphosphate (ATP)

10   *The role of the centriole is to:*
(A)   produce protein and lipid for the cell membrane
(B)   generate energy for the cell's activities
(C)   regulate the cellular activities using information stored in DNA
(D)   facilitate chromosome movement during cell division
(E)   break down lipid and foreign protein from ingested debris

11   *A defect in mitochondrial DNA is most likely to cause:*
(A)   problems with energy production in the cell
(B)   problems with cellular division
(C)   defective protein synthesis
(D)   abnormal degradation of cellular debris
(E)   no problem at all

12   *Cells with cilia are usually found in the:*
(A)   epidermis of skin
(B)   gut lining
(C)   bladder lining
(D)   paranasal sinuses
(E)   ventricles of the brain

13   *Cells with microvilli are usually found in the:*
(A)   cerebral cortex
(B)   lining of the small intestine
(C)   lining of the trachea
(D)   interior of the spleen
(E)   wall of the urinary bladder

14   *Which of the following cell types would have a flagellum?*
(A)   respiratory epithelium
(B)   choroid plexus of lateral ventricle
(C)   kidney epithelial cell
(D)   lining of duodenum
(E)   spermatozoon

Mitochondrial disease

Mitochondria are the powerhouses of the cell and may be derived from microorganisms, which took up symbiotic residence inside our ancestral cells during early evolution. Mitochondria have their own DNA, and defects in that can cause significant disease. Mitochondria are present in all cells except red blood cells, so the effects of mitochondrial disease are widespread and serious: muscle weakness, neurological problems, learning disorders, early-onset dementia, heart dysfunction, liver and kidney disease. Treatment is difficult, but future avenues could involve transfer of normal genes to affected individuals (gene therapy).

Colour and label

*i) Label each structure shown on
the illustrations*

Cell Structure

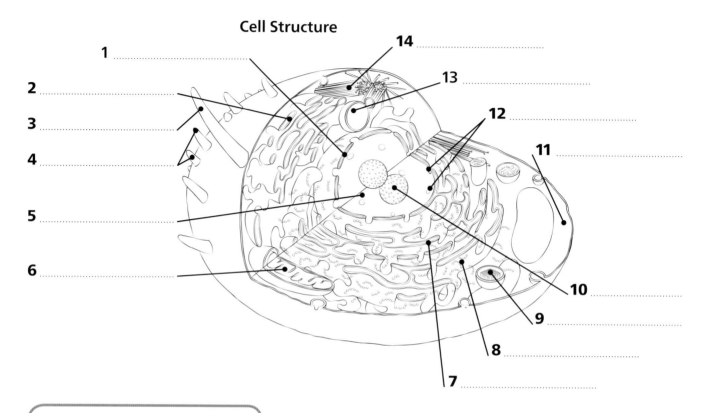

1 ....

2 ....

3 ....

4 ....

5 ....

6 ....

14 ....

13 ....

12 ....

11 ....

10 ....

9 ....

8 ....

7 ....

---

*ii) Use the key to colour the
structures below*

▥ Myelin sheath

▤ Cell body

▦ Nucleolus

Neuron

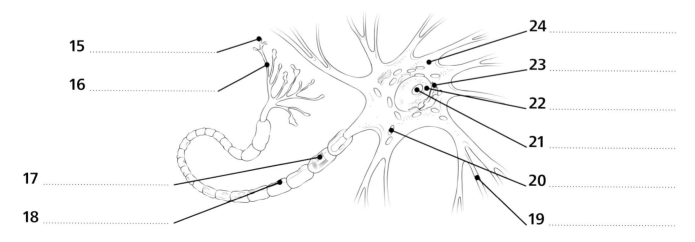

15 ....

16 ....

17 ....

18 ....

24 ....

23 ....

22 ....

21 ....

20 ....

19 ....

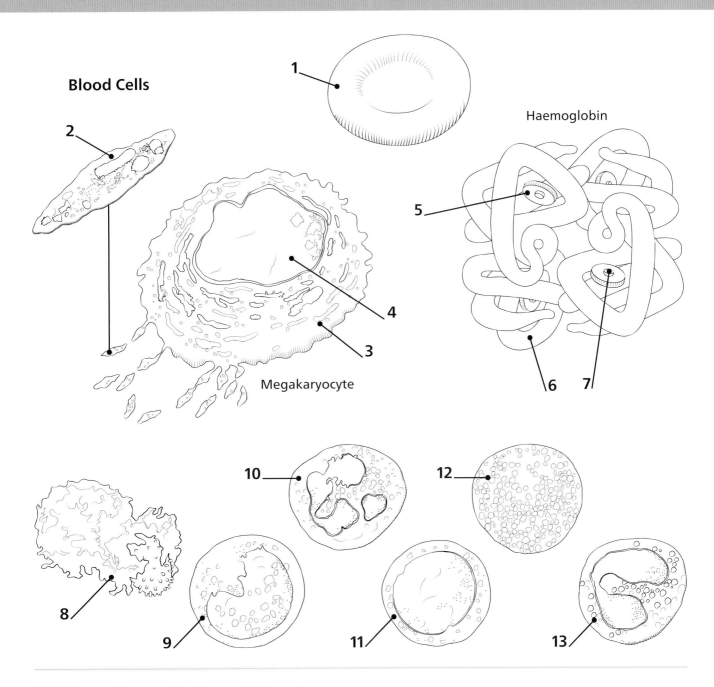

Blood Cells

Haemoglobin

Megakaryocyte

i) Add numbers to the boxes below to match each label to the correct part of the artwork

Globin protein strand	☐	Macrophage	☐
Cytoplasm	☐	Nucleus	☐
Eosinophil	☐	Iron ion	☐
Monocyte	☐	Neutrophil	☐
Red blood cell	☐	Basophil	☐
Haem	☐	Platelet	☐
Lymphocyte	☐		

Multiple choice

1 *Which of the following is NOT a type of connective tissue?*

(A) bone
(B) tendon
(C) blood
(D) sweat gland ✓
(E) adipose tissue (fat)

2 *Which of the following is NOT a type of epithelial tissue?*

(A) sweat gland
(B) sebaceous gland
(C) adipose tissue ✓
(D) cornea
(E) olfactory mucosa

3 *Which of the following is a defining feature of epithelial tissue?*

(A) it is exquisitely sensitive to touch
(B) it is found only on the exterior of the body
(C) it always consists of a single layer of cells
(D) it has no secretory function ✓
(E) it covers the internal and external body surfaces

4 *Which of the following would be an example of loose connective tissue?*

(A) tendon
(B) ligament
(C) subcutaneous tissue ✓
(D) an aponeurosis
(E) blood serum

5 *The role of dense connective tissue is to:*

(A) resist tensile forces and store potential energy
(B) provide a storage site for lipids and calcium
(C) produce voluntary movement under command from the brain
(D) resist compressive forces during jumping
(E) both A and D are correct

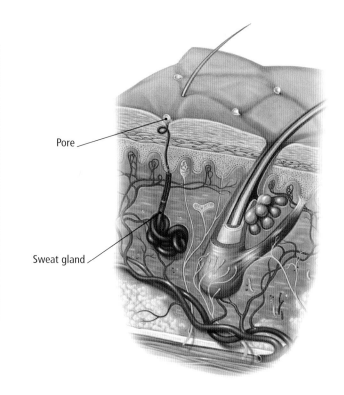

Pore

Sweat gland

Sweat Gland

Involved in temperature regulation, the sweat glands release sweat to the surface of the skin, which cools the skin as it evaporates.

6 *Which of the following is an example of peripheral nervous system tissue?*

(A) dorsal root (spinal) ganglion
(B) cerebral cortex
(C) autonomic ganglion
(D) spinal cord grey matter
(E) both A and C are correct

7 *Which of the following statements is true concerning fat?*

(A) it consists of brown and yellow types
(B) it can develop directly from muscle cells
(C) it is often deposited inside the fluid of the peritoneal cavity
(D) it is richly supplied with blood
(E) none of the above is correct

8   *Which of the following is true concerning muscle tissue?*

(A)   it includes voluntary smooth muscle

(B)   smooth muscle can beat rhythmically at up to 150 times per minute

(C)   the heart contains voluntary muscle

(D)   both skeletal and cardiac muscle are striated

(E)   smooth muscle has a richer blood supply than cardiac muscle

9   *Elastic cartilage is found in which parts of the body?*

(A)   external ear

(B)   synovial joint surface

(C)   external nose

(D)   pubic symphysis

(E)   both A and C are correct

10   *Fibrocartilage is found in which parts of the body?*

(A)   head of femur

(B)   intervertebral disk

(C)   heart

(D)   external ear

(E)   skull

Where does cancer come from?

Cancer is more likely to come from some tissue types than others. Most cancers arise from epithelial tissue, because it lies at the body surface (e.g. skin, airways and gut lining), and is constantly exposed to cancer-causing agents (carcinogens). Normal epithelial tissues are also actively dividing, so any cancer-causing gene (oncogene) is likely to lead to a rapidly growing tumour. Cancers may also arise from cells in bone, muscle or fat (osteosarcoma, myosarcoma, liposarcoma) but this is less common.

11   *Where is brown fat usually found?*

(A)   between the shoulder blades of newborns

(B)   in the medullary cavities of bone

(C)   in the mesenteries of the abdomen

(D)   in the capsule of the spleen

(E)   between the lymph nodes of the mediastinum

12   *Approximately what percentage of body weight is made up of skeletal muscle in a person of healthy body mass index?*

(A)   10 per cent

(B)   20 per cent

(C)   30 per cent

(D)   40 per cent

(E)   50 per cent

13   *Which of the following tissue types is a good thermal insulator?*

(A)   skeletal muscle

(B)   nervous tissue

(C)   adipose tissue

(D)   epidermal tissue

(E)   endocrine tissue

14   *Which of the following tissue has the highest metabolic demand when the body is at rest?*

(A)   adipose tissue

(B)   gut wall

(C)   lung tissue

(D)   tongue muscle

(E)   brain tissue

Colour and label

i) Label each structure shown on the illustrations

Skin

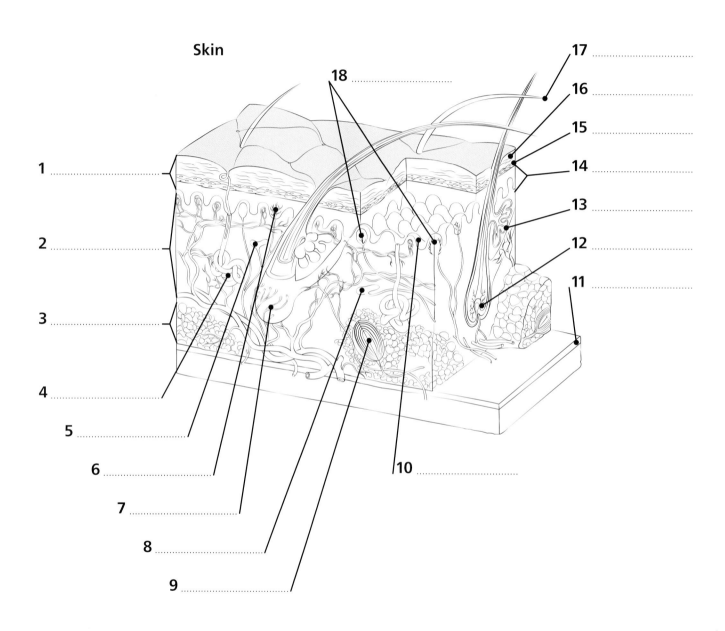

Nail

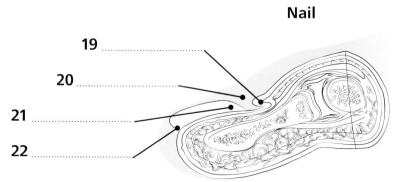

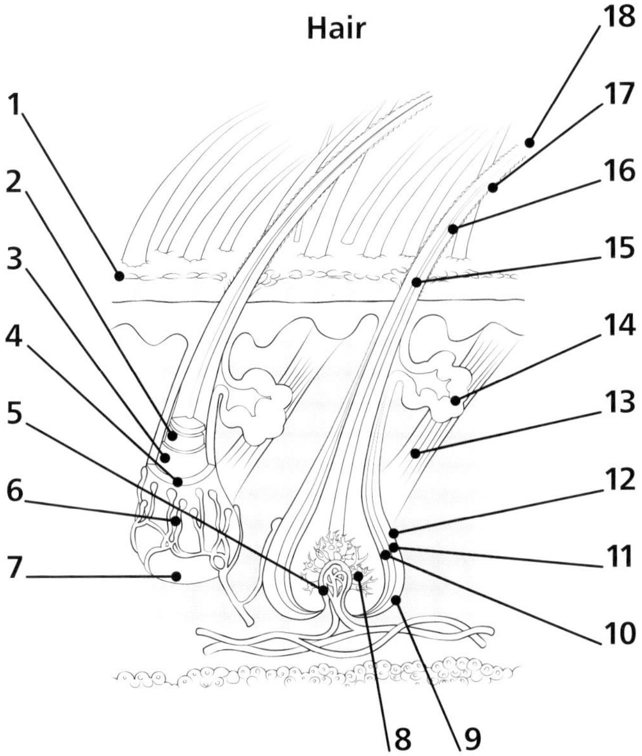

Hair

1
2
3
4
5
6
7
8 9
10
11
12
13
14
15
16
17
18

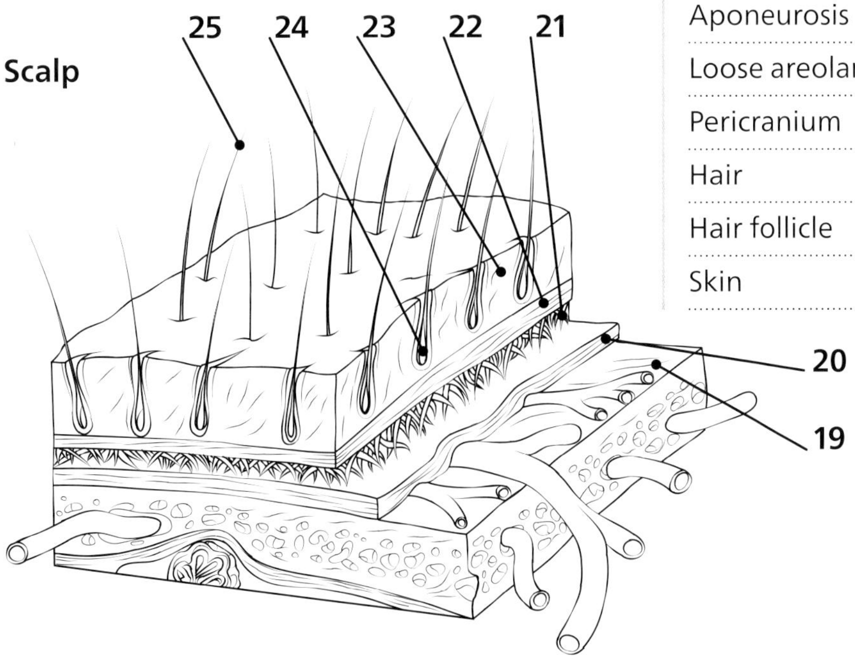

i) Add numbers to the boxes below to match each label to the correct part of the artwork

Nerve	☐
Medulla	☐
Internal root sheath	☐
Cuticle	☐
Dermal hair papilla	☐
Epidermis	☐
Follicle sheath	☐
Hair bulb	☐
Melanocyte	☐
Internal root sheath	☐
Erector pili muscle (arrector pili)	☐
Follicle sheath	☐
Skull bone	☐
Sebaceous gland	☐
Precuticular epithelium	☐
Cortex	☐
External root sheath	☐
Hair shaft	☐
External root sheaths	☐
Aponeurosis	☐
Loose areolar tissue	☐
Pericranium	☐
Hair	☐
Hair follicle	☐
Skin	☐

Scalp

25 24 23 22 21

20

19

Fill in the blanks

1   The correct anatomical term for the region between the shoulder and elbow is the

_____.

2   The _____ is the region where the umbilical cord attached during prenatal life.

3   The _____ region is at the junction of the anterior abdominal wall and the lower limb.

4   The correct anatomical term for the region between the elbow and the wrist is the

_____.

5   The _____ is a standard position of the body and its parts for use when describing anatomical structures.

6   In anatomical terminology, the _____ is the region between the knee and the ankle.

7   The _____ is the region between the proximal arm and the chest wall.

8   The term _____ is used to refer to the neck.

9   The depression posterior to the knee is called the _____ fossa.

10   The anatomical term for the thumb (digit 1) is the _____.

11   The body cavity that encloses the heart is called the _____.

12   The _____ system is made up of a series of glands that secrete mainly into the bloodstream.

13   The inferior surface of the foot is called the _____ surface.

14 The _____ protects the rest of the body against radiation, heat loss, abrasion and microorganisms.

15 The _____ fossa is the space anterior to the elbow when the body is in the anatomical position.

16 Free _____ have the ability to use messenger RNA to construct protein molecules.

17 Nerve cells are characterised by having an _____ to convey nerve impulses away from the cell body.

18 Between cell divisions, the cell's DNA and associated proteins are dispersed within the nucleus as _____.

19 The body fibre type that has optimal elastic properties is _____.

20 The protein _____ makes up the bulk of connective tissue and is a key component of bone.

Osteogenesis imperfecta

Bone tissue depends for its strength and resilience on the blending of biological fibre (mainly collagen) and mineral crystals (hydroxyapatite). Osteogenesis imperfecta is a rare but serious genetic disease (affecting around 7 people per 100,000) where bone strength is impaired due to defective production of collagen. In milder cases the condition leads to increased risk of fractures, hearing loss and a blue or grey tint to the sclera of the eyeball. In severe cases, the fractures may be so common as to cause short stature, serious disability, dental abnormalities and respiratory problems.

Meissner corpuscles   Hair
Free nerve ending
Ruffini endings
Epidermis
Dermis
Subcutaneous fat
Sweat gland
Nerve endings
Krause bulb
Pacinian corpuscle

Horny layer (stratum corneum)
Stratum granulosum
Stratum germinativum and spinosum
Sebaceous gland
Subcutaneous fat
Deep fascia
Hair follicle
Dermal hair papilla

Skin

The skin is the largest organ, forming a protective layer over the internal organs, and protecting against external elements. The three layers of tissue that make up the skin are the epidermis, dermis, and subcutaneous tissue.

Match the statement to the reason

1 Scholars of anatomy can always reliably describe the position of body parts to other anatomists because …

a component glands secrete hormones into the blood stream for distribution throughout the body.

2 The endocrine system can act on diverse parts of the body because …

b lubricating fluid from the joint space can enter or leave the tissue depending on joint loading.

3 Cardiac muscle has a striated appearance under the microscope because …

c they use a standard anatomical position and agreed terminology when communicating their findings.

4 Scars often become white with time because …

d collagenous connective tissue is formed as an important stage in tissue repair.

5 Hyaline cartilage is an ideal tissue to cover the surfaces of joints because …

e component cells have regularly arranged contractile proteins that can slide past each other.

Components of Blood

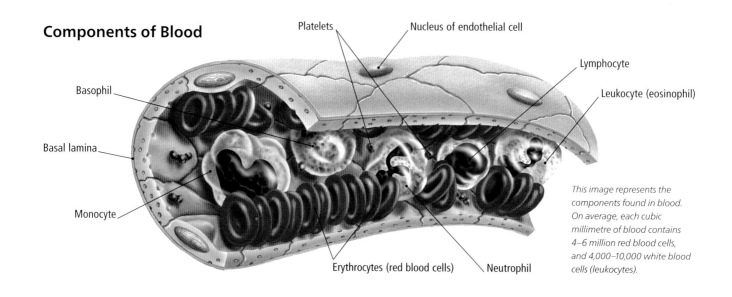

Platelets

Nucleus of endothelial cell

Lymphocyte

Basophil

Leukocyte (eosinophil)

Basal lamina

Monocyte

Erythrocytes (red blood cells)

Neutrophil

This image represents the components found in blood. On average, each cubic millimetre of blood contains 4–6 million red blood cells, and 4,000–10,000 white blood cells (leukocytes).

1 Bone combines the features of mechanical strength and resistance to cracking because …

a it is a highly flexible type of tissue that allows these body parts to deform, but return to their original shape and size.

2 Blood is regarded as a connective tissue because …

b it consists of cellular components (red and white blood cells, platelets) embedded in a fluid matrix (plasma) containing dissolved proteins, lipoproteins, nutrients, hormones and gases.

3 Elastic cartilage is found in the external ear (auricle or pinna) and the nose because …

c it consists of nerve cells (neurons) connected to each other by axons that are coated with a fatty layer (myelin) that increases the speed of conduction.

4 The cells of the immune system are in an excellent position to provide surveillance of the body's tissues for invading microorganisms and cancer because …

d it is a composite material consisting of organic fibres (mostly the protein collagen) embedded in a mineral matrix (hydroxyapatite).

5 Neural (nervous) tissue provides a means of rapid internal communication within the body because …

e they are distributed in nodular structures (lymph nodes) along the lymphatic channels that drain excess tissue fluid back towards the venous side of the circulation.

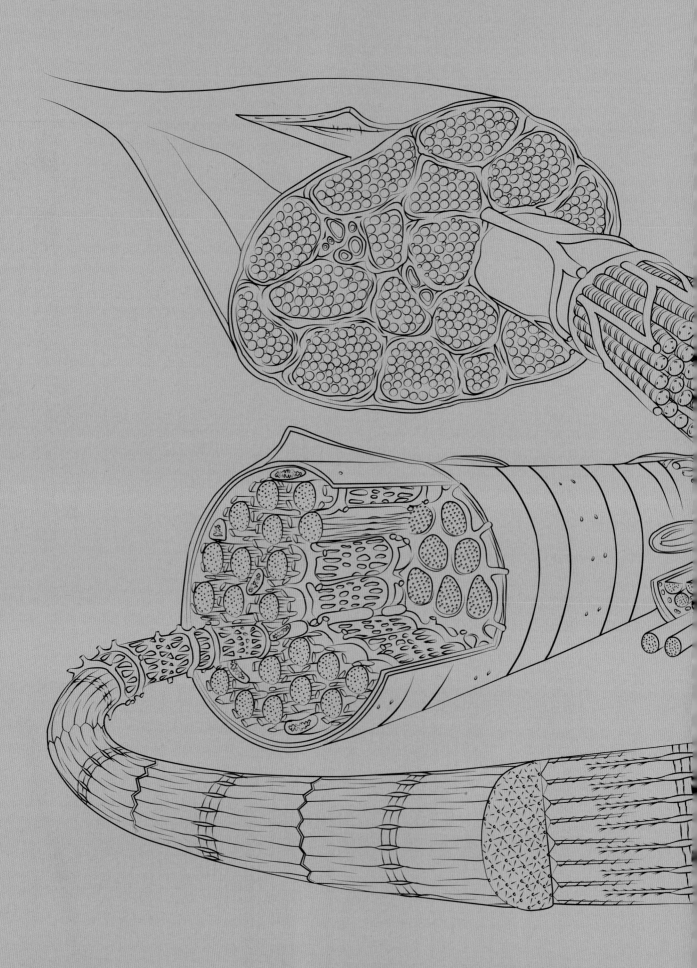

CHAPTER 2: THE MUSCULOSKELETAL SYSTEM

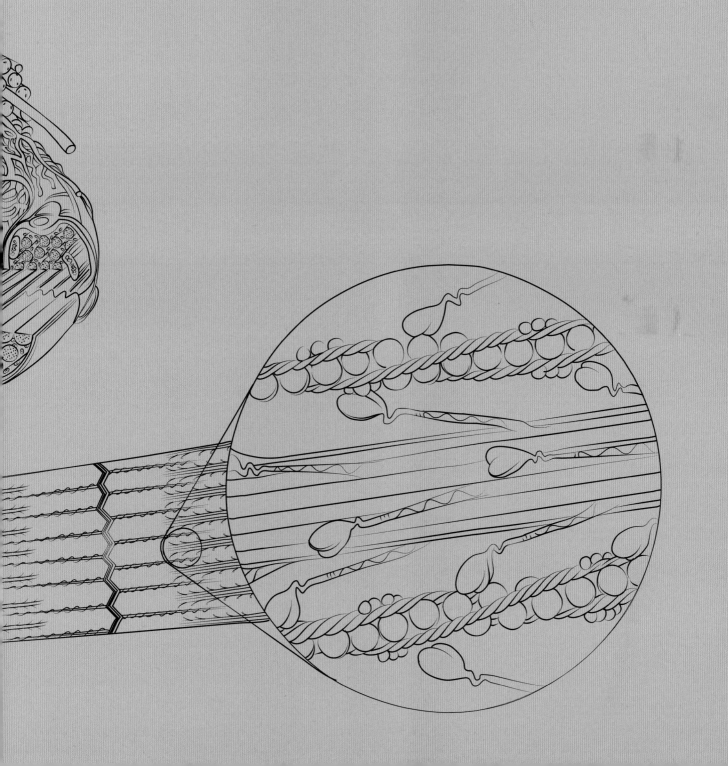

Axial Skeleton and Joints

The axial skeleton consists of the skull, hyoid bone, vertebral column, ribs and sternum. The role of the axial skeleton is primarily to protect the nervous system and other visceral organs. The limb bones (appendicular skeleton) attach to the axial skeleton by only the sternoclavicular joint for the upper limb and the strong sacroiliac joint for the lower limb. Joints between components of the axial skeleton may be synovial in type, but are of relatively low mobility.

Key terms:

Acromion The distal end of the spine of the scapula. Forms a synovial joint with the distal clavicle and provides attachment for the coracoacromial ligament and deltoid muscle.

Anterior nasal (piriform) aperture The front opening of the bony nasal cavity of the skull.

Atlas (C1) The first cervical vertebra.

Axis (C2) The second cervical vertebra.

Cervical vertebrae Region of the vertebral column formed by seven vertebrae (C1–C7). The upper two in order are named the atlas and axis, respectively.

Clavicles The paired bones forming the anterior parts of each shoulder girdle. The clavicles form struts, which allow the scapulae to move around the thoracic cage.

Coccyx The terminal part of the vertebral column. It is a vestigial tail with only four or five segments.

Costal cartilage Bars of hyaline cartilage that attach to the anterior ends of the ribs. Cartilages 1–7 connect directly to the sternum; 8–10 articulate with the cartilage above; 11 and 12 have no connection with the sternum at all.

False ribs (pairs 8–10) Ribs that have only an indirect connection with the sternum.

Floating ribs (pairs 11 & 12) Ribs that have no connection with the sternum, either directly or indirectly.

Frontal bone The bone underlying the forehead.

Humerus The bone of the upper arm.

Ilium One of the three component bones of the hip. It has a flared crest or wing superiorly and a body inferiorly.

Lower teeth In an adult, each side has two incisors, one canine, two premolars, and three molars.

Lumbar vertebra Vertebrae of the lower back. Each lumbar vertebra has a large body, short thick laminae, and pedicles and mammillary processes extending backward from the superior articular processes.

Mandible The bone of the lower jaw. It has an alveolar margin to support the teeth, paired condylar processes for articulation with the temporal bone, and paired coronoid processes.

Maxilla The bone of the medial cheek. It contributes to the inferior margin of the orbit and support of the upper teeth.

Occipital bone The large bone on the underside of the skull. It provides attachment for the post-vertebral muscles of the neck and bears occipital condyles for articulation with the atlas (cervical vertebra 1).

Orbit The bony cavity containing the eye, lacrimal gland, extraocular muscles, nerves, vessels, and orbital fat. Bounded by the maxilla, frontal, sphenoid, ethmoid, and lacrimal bones.

Parietal bone A flat bone of the braincase (calvaria). It articulates with the frontal, temporal, sphenoid, and occipital bones.

Sacrum The large fused part of the vertebral column that attaches to the ilium of the hip bone.

Scapula The posterior bone of the shoulder girdle. It has anterior and posterior surfaces; medial, lateral, and superior borders; and coracoid and acromial processes. The glenoid fossa makes a joint with the humerus.

Spinous processes The posteriorly projecting processes of vertebrae.

Sternum The bone in the front wall of the chest, forming part of the skeleton of the thorax. It consists of the manubrium, body, and xiphoid process.

Temporal bone The temporal bone has squamous, tympanic, styloid, mastoid, and petrous parts.

Thoracic vertebra A vertebra of the thoracic region. Typical thoracic vertebrae have superior and inferior demifacets on the body for articulation with the rib heads and long transverse processes with facets for articulation with the tubercles of ribs.

Transverse processes The transverse processes of vertebrae extend laterally from the junction of the laminae and pedicles of the neural arch.

True ribs (pairs 1–7) Ribs that have a direct connection (through their costal cartilages) to the sternum.

Upper teeth In an adult, each side has two incisors, one canine, two premolars, and three molars.

Zygomatic bone The bone of the upper lateral cheek. It articulates with the maxilla, temporal, and frontal bones.

Axial Skeleton – anterior view

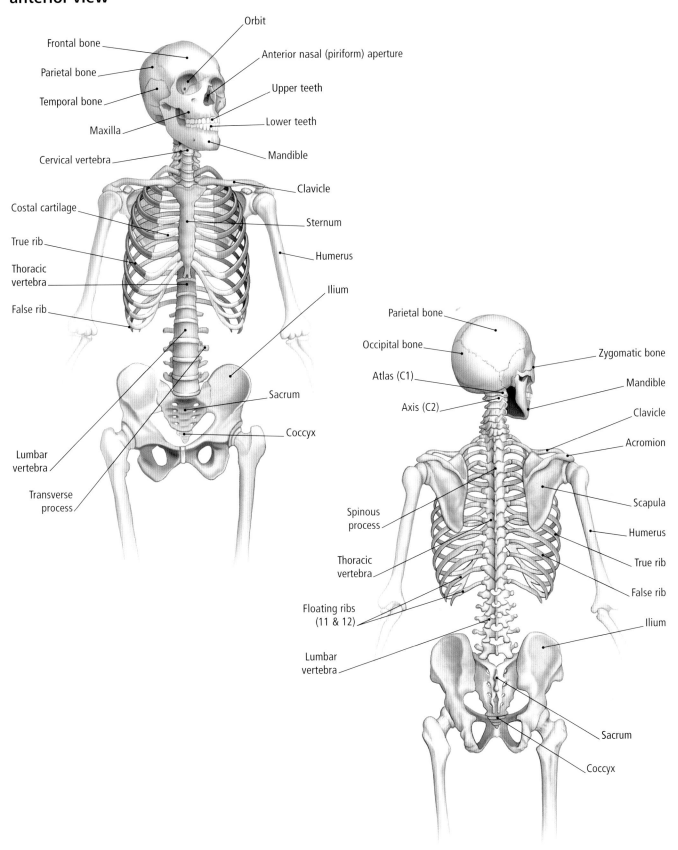

Orbit

Frontal bone

Parietal bone

Temporal bone

Maxilla

Cervical vertebra

Costal cartilage

True rib

Thoracic vertebra

False rib

Lumbar vertebra

Transverse process

Anterior nasal (piriform) aperture

Upper teeth

Lower teeth

Mandible

Clavicle

Sternum

Humerus

Ilium

Sacrum

Coccyx

Parietal bone

Occipital bone

Atlas (C1)

Axis (C2)

Spinous process

Thoracic vertebra

Floating ribs (11 & 12)

Lumbar vertebra

Zygomatic bone

Mandible

Clavicle

Acromion

Scapula

Humerus

True rib

False rib

Ilium

Sacrum

Coccyx

Axial Skeleton – posterior view

Bones and Joints of the Upper Limb

The upper limb bones consist of a pectoral girdle (scapula and clavicle), which has a relatively loose attachment to the axial skeleton by way of the shoulder muscles and the synovial sternoclavicular joint, the single bone of the arm (humerus), bones of the forearm (radius and ulna), wrist bones (the eight carpal bones), palm bones (metacarpals) and finger bones or phalanges (two only in digit one, but three in each of the other digits).

Key terms:

Acromioclavicular joint The plane joint between the acromion of the scapula and the distal end of the clavicle. The articular surfaces are predominantly fibrocartilaginous.

Acromion The distal end of the spine of the scapula. It forms a synovial joint with the distal clavicle and provides attachment for the coracoacromial ligament and the deltoid muscle.

Carpal bones The eight bones of the wrist. The proximal row (from lateral to medial) comprises the scaphoid, lunate, triquetrum, and pisiform. The distal row comprises the trapezium, trapezoid, capitate, and hamate.

Clavicle See pp. 38–9

Coracoid process An anterior process of the scapula. It provides attachment for the short head of the biceps brachii and pectoralis minor muscles.

Glenoid cavity The cavity of the glenohumeral synovial joint (shoulder joint) between the glenoid fossa of the scapula and the head of the humerus.

Glenoid fossa The shallow articular surface of the lateral angle of the scapula. It engages in a synovial joint with the head of the humerus (glenohumeral or shoulder joint).

Greater tubercle of humerus The elevation on the lateral humerus that provides attachment for the supraspinatus, infraspinatus, and teres minor muscles.

Head of humerus The articular surface of the proximal humerus. It is slightly less than a hemisphere and is surrounded by the anatomical neck.

Humerus The bone of the arm. It consists of a shaft and proximal and distal articular surfaces.

Lateral border of scapula The lateral edge of the scapula. It provides attachment for the long head of the triceps brachii (at the infraglenoid tubercle), teres minor, and teres major muscles.

Lesser tubercle A roughened elevation of the anterior proximal humerus.

Medial border of scapula The medial edge of the scapula. It provides attachment for the levator scapulae, rhomboid minor, and rhomboid major muscles.

Metacarpal bones The bones of the palm. They are numbered from 1 to 5, from the thumb to the little finger. The space between the metacarpals is filled by muscles.

Phalanges The bones of the digits. There are two (proximal and distal) in digit 1 (the thumb) and three (proximal, middle, and distal) in digits 2–5. Singular: phalanx.

Radius The lateral bone of the forearm. It engages in a pivot synovial joint with the ulna, allowing rotational movements of the radius around the ulna (pronation and supination).

Scapula The posterior bone of the shoulder girdle. It has anterior and posterior surfaces; medial, lateral, and superior borders; and coracoid and acromial processes. The glenoid fossa makes a joint with the humerus.

Shoulder joint The glenohumeral (shoulder) synovial joint. It is a freely mobile ball-and-socket joint, which is stabilised by the joint capsule and muscles of the rotator cuff group (including supraspinatus, infraspinatus, and teres minor).

Spine of scapula The laterally running sharp elevation of the posterior scapula. It separates the supraspinous and infraspinous fossae.

Subscapular fossa The concave, anterior surface of the scapula. It provides attachment for the subscapularis, a muscle that medially rotates the arm.

Superior border of scapula The thin and sharp upper border of the scapula. It is interrupted at its junction with the coracoid process by the scapular notch, which transmits the suprascapular nerve.

Ulna The medial bone of the forearm. It articulates with the humerus proximally (humeroulnar synovial joint of the elbow) and engages in a pivot joint with the radius (proximal and distal radioulnar synovial joints).

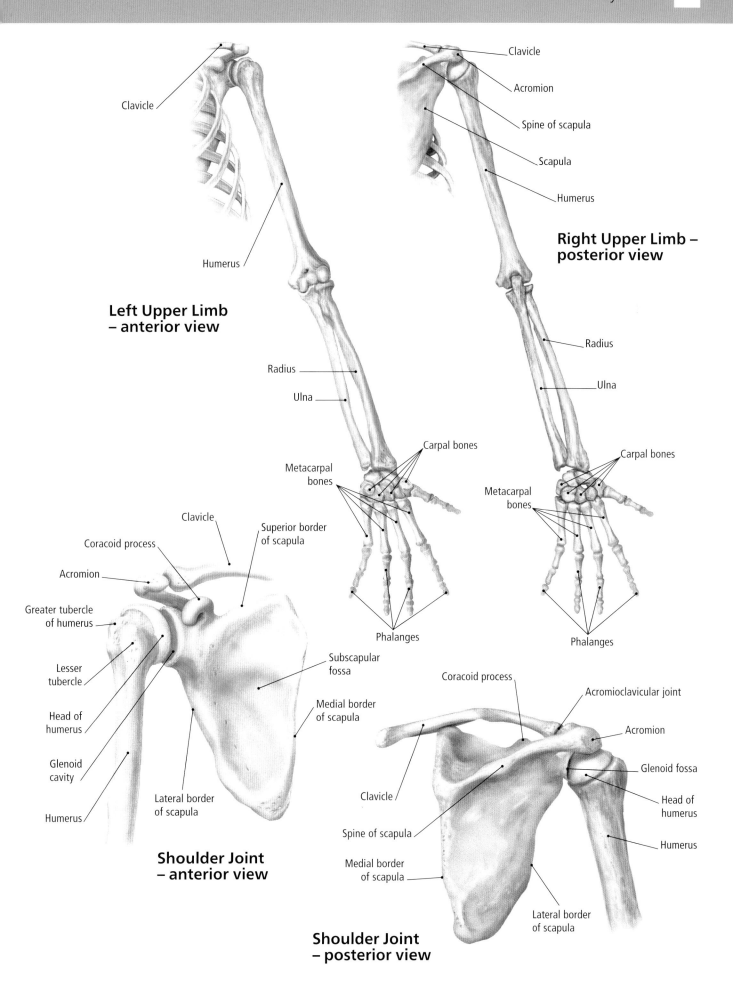

Clavicle

**Left Upper Limb
– anterior view**

Humerus

Clavicle

Acromion

Spine of scapula

Scapula

Humerus

**Right Upper Limb –
posterior view**

Radius

Radius

Ulna

Ulna

Carpal bones

Metacarpal
bones

Carpal bones

Metacarpal
bones

Phalanges

Phalanges

Coracoid process

Clavicle

Superior border
of scapula

Acromion

Greater tubercle
of humerus

Lesser
tubercle

Subscapular
fossa

Head of
humerus

Medial border
of scapula

Glenoid
cavity

Lateral border
of scapula

Humerus

**Shoulder Joint
– anterior view**

Coracoid process

Acromioclavicular joint

Acromion

Glenoid fossa

Clavicle

Head of
humerus

Spine of scapula

Medial border
of scapula

Humerus

Lateral border
of scapula

**Shoulder Joint
– posterior view**

Bones and Joints of the Lower Limb

The lower limb bones include the hip bone or os coxa (ilium, ischium and pubis together), joining at the acetabulum, which attaches to the sacrum at the sacroiliac joint, the single bone of the thigh (femur), the paired bones of the leg (robust tibia and pin-like fibula), the seven tarsal bones (talus, calcaneus, cuboid, navicular and three cuneiforms), five metatarsals and 14 toe bones (two in the great toe, but three in each of the other digits).

Key terms:

Adductor tubercle A prominent elevation on the uppermost part of the medial femoral condyle.

Anterior border The ridge of the tibia at the front of the shin.

Anterior intercondylar area This region is between the paired articular facets of the anterior tibial plateau.

Apex of fibula The upper end of the fibula. It has one of the ligaments that runs alongside the knee joint attached to it.

Articular facet for talus The fibula contributes to the lateral part of the ankle joint. Its lower end articulates with the lateral surface of the trochlea of the talus.

Articular facet of medial malleolus The distal tibia forms the medial part of the ankle joint and has articular cartilage.

Articular surface with head of fibula A flat, circular facet on the lateral condyle of the tibia for articulation with the head of the fibula.

Calcaneus The bone of the heel, also known as os calcis. Has articular surfaces on upper surface for the talus and cuboid.

Femur The bone of the thigh.

Fibula A slender bone on the lateral leg that bears no weight.

Fibular notch The notch on the lateral surface of the distal tibia for articulation with the fibula.

Fovea capitis A depression in the head of the femur for attachment of the ligament of the head of the femur.

Greater trochanter A large protrusion on the proximal femur. It provides attachment for the gluteus medius and gluteus minimus muscles.

Head of femur The ball-shaped proximal end of the femur that fits into the hip joint socket (acetabulum).

Head of fibula The expanded proximal part of the fibula. Has a circular articular facet for the lateral condyle of the tibia.

Inferior articular surface Inferior surface of the tibia for articulation with superior surface of trochlea of the talus.

Intercondylar eminence An elevation in the centre of the tibia. The cruciate ligaments within the knee and the menisci, which help the joint surfaces conform, attach to the tibia immediately in front and behind it.

Intercondylar fossa The depression between the medial and lateral condyles of the femur.

Interosseous border The sharp lateral border of the tibia.

Lateral condyle The lateral part of the expanded upper end of the tibia.

Lateral epicondyle A prominence on the lateral surface of the lateral femoral condyle.

Lateral malleolus The inferior end of the fibula forms the lateral malleolus of the ankle.

Lateral surface The lateral surface of the tibia has the tibialis anterior muscle attached to it.

Lesser trochanter An elevation from the back of the junction of the neck and shaft of the femur.

Medial condyle The medial part of the expanded upper end of the tibia. Articulates with the medial condyle of femur.

Medial epicondyle A prominence on the medial surface of the medial femoral condyle.

Medial malleolus The medial prominence of the ankle, formed by the distal tibia.

Metatarsal bones The five bones of the forefoot.

Neck of femur The part of the femur between the head of the femur and the greater trochanter.

Neck of fibula The narrow upper part of the fibula immediately distal to the head.

Patella The kneecap. It is a triangular sesamoid bone embedded in the tendon of the quadriceps femoris muscle.

Patellar surface The articular surface on the distal femur for the patella.

Phalanges The bones of the digits.

Shaft (diaphysis) of femur Main tubular part of the femur.

Superior articular surfaces (medial and lateral facets) The paired articular facets of the upper tibia.

Talus The most superior tarsal bone. It comprises a head, neck, and body.

Tarsal bones The tarsal bones include the talus, calcaneus, navicular, cuboid, and three cuneiforms.

Tibia The larger weight-bearing bone of the leg.

Tibial tuberosity An elevation on the anterior margin of the proximal tibia.

Right Lower Limb – anterior view

Left Lower Limb – posterior view

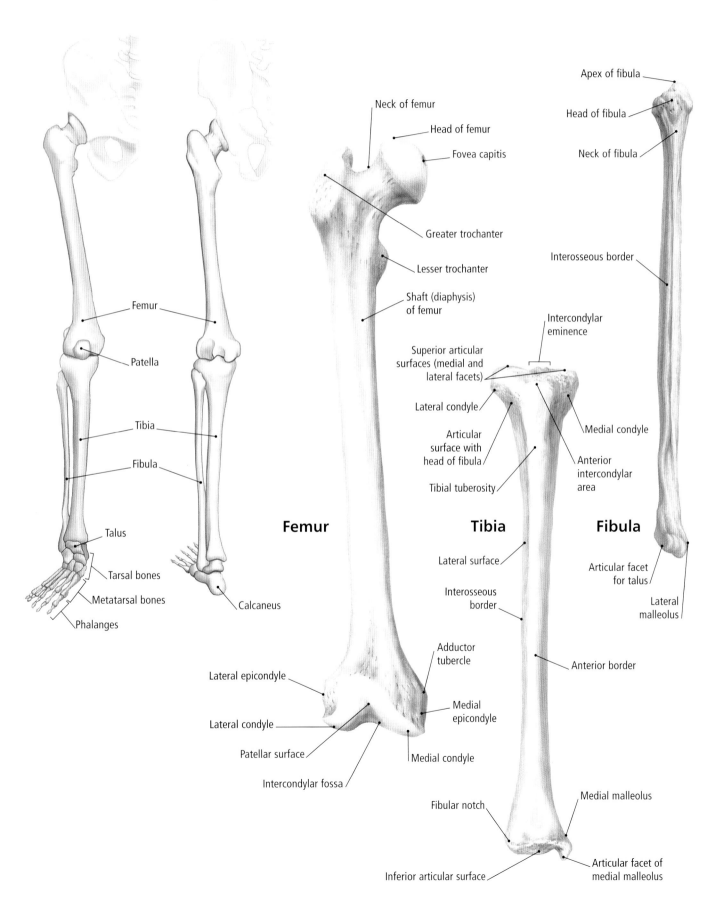

Femur

Patella

Tibia

Fibula

Talus

Tarsal bones

Metatarsal bones

Phalanges

Calcaneus

Femur

Neck of femur

Head of femur

Fovea capitis

Greater trochanter

Lesser trochanter

Shaft (diaphysis) of femur

Lateral epicondyle

Lateral condyle

Patellar surface

Intercondylar fossa

Adductor tubercle

Medial epicondyle

Medial condyle

Tibia

Superior articular surfaces (medial and lateral facets)

Lateral condyle

Articular surface with head of fibula

Tibial tuberosity

Intercondylar eminence

Medial condyle

Anterior intercondylar area

Lateral surface

Interosseous border

Fibular notch

Inferior articular surface

Anterior border

Medial malleolus

Fibula

Apex of fibula

Head of fibula

Neck of fibula

Interosseous border

Articular facet for talus

Lateral malleolus

Articular facet of medial malleolus

True or false?

1   The axial skeleton includes the skull, vertebral column, ribs, sternum and hyoid bone.

T

2   The hyoid bone is in direct contact with the vertebral column.

Supported by Muscles & long
ligaments only

F

3   There are three pairs of floating ribs that have no contact with the sternum.

F

4   The five lumbar vertebrae allow free rotation of the trunk.

F/E/SF ONly.

F

5   Fusion of the five sacral vertebrae occurs in early adult life.

T

6   Bones of the pectoral girdle include the scapula, clavicle and humerus.

F

7   The humerus is expanded distally as the capitulum and trochlea.

T

8   The radial tuberosity lies towards the proximal end of the radius.

T

9   The bones in the proximal row of the carpus are the scaphoid, lunate, triquetrum and pisiform.

T

10   The bones of the palm are collectively called the metatarsals.   *Metacarpals*

F

11   The three bones that make up the hip bone (os coxa) are the ilium, ischium and pubis.

T

12   The components of the hip bone meet at the pubic symphysis.   *Acetabulum*

F

13   The structure on which we sit is the ischial spine.   *tuberosity*

F

14   The femur has a proximal rounded head that fits into the acetabulum.

T

15   The shaft of the femur angles inwards towards the knee joint.

T

16 *The distal end of the femur has two condyles, each with an elliptical cross-section.*

17 *The thickest bone of the leg is the tibia.*

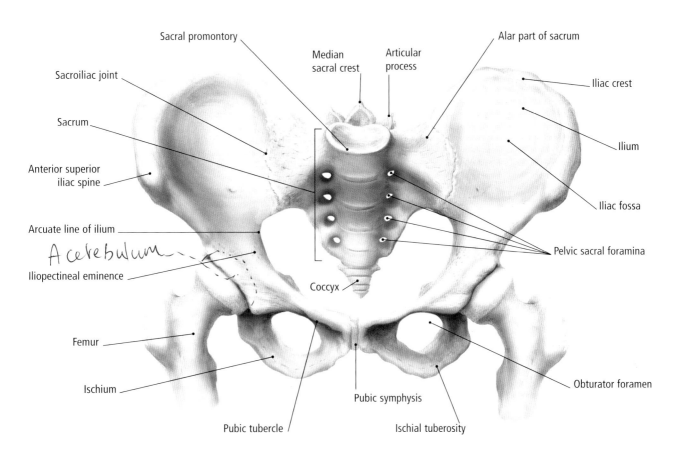

Sacral promontory

Median sacral crest

Articular process

Alar part of sacrum

Sacroiliac joint

Iliac crest

Sacrum

Ilium

Anterior superior iliac spine

Iliac fossa

Arcuate line of ilium

A cerebulum

Pelvic sacral foramina

Iliopectineal eminence

Coccyx

Femur

Ischium

Obturator foramen

Pubic symphysis

Pubic tubercle

Ischial tuberosity

Female Pelvis – anterior view

While the components of the male and female pelvis are the same, the shape and dimensions differ. The male pelvis is generally larger to meet the demands of heavier weight. The female pelvic inlet is wider to allow the passage of the baby's head during childbirth.

Fractured neck of femur

The proximal femur has an almost spherical head supported on a narrow neck. Fractures of the neck of the femur are common, particularly in the osteoporotic elderly and in motor vehicle accidents. There is often compression of the fracture site, so limb shortening and rotation are common. The femoral head is also vulnerable to necrosis in this type of fracture, because much of its blood supply passes through the femoral neck. Femoral neck fractures may require complete surgical replacement of the femoral head, neck and acetabulum (prosthetic hip) or pinning of the fracture site.

Multiple choice

1 *Which of the following is NOT a component bone of the skull?*
(A) temporal
(B) sphenoid
(C) hyoid ✓
(D) vomer
(E) lacrimal

2 *Which of the following groups of bones contribute to the walls of the cranial cavity?*
(A) frontal, sphenoid and vomer
(B) parietal, temporal and zygomatic
(C) occipital, parietal and nasal
(D) axis, frontal and parietal
(E) mandible, sphenoid and occipital

3 *Which of the following bones carries the upper teeth?*
(A) palatine
(B) sphenoid
(C) ethmoid
(D) maxilla
(E) none of the above is correct

4 *Which of the following statements is correct concerning the adult (permanent) teeth?*
(A) there are 20 in total
(B) there are 8 incisors in total
(C) the last premolars are called the wisdom teeth
(D) canines are located between premolars and molars
(E) molars have only one root

5 *The number of ribs that directly connect with the sternum, i.e. the true ribs, is:*
(A) 3
(B) 5
(C) 7
(D) 9
(E) 12

6 *Which of the following is correct concerning the false ribs?*
(A) they connect to the costal cartilages of ribs above
(B) they protect the kidneys
(C) they directly attach to the xiphoid process
(D) they are purely cartilaginous in adults
(E) both A and D are correct

7 *The humerus has a smooth, rounded head that is surrounded by a rim called the:*
(A) surgical neck
(B) capitulum
(C) glenoid labrum
(D) spiral line
(E) anatomical neck

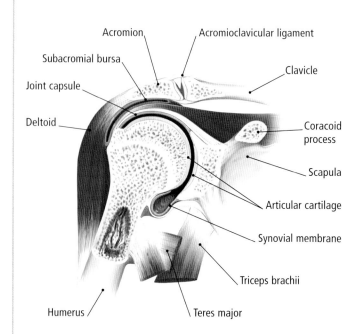

Shoulder – cross-section

The smooth movements achieved by the shoulder are the result of several factors. A small contact area between the articulation surfaces and a generous, well-lubricated joint capsule provide friction-free movement.

8   *The surgical neck of the humerus is the place where:*

Ⓐ   the radial nerve passes posterior to the humeral shaft
Ⓑ   the humerus is highly prone to fracture
Ⓒ   the brachial artery is a close relation of the humeral shaft
Ⓓ   surgeons can remove bone for grafting
Ⓔ   most of the triceps major muscle attaches

9   *The ulna articulates with which part of the humerus?*

Ⓐ   capitulum
Ⓑ   trochlea
Ⓒ   head
Ⓓ   medial epicondyle
Ⓔ   none of the above is correct

10   *The bone that directly articulates with the distal radius is the:*

Ⓐ   scaphoid
Ⓑ   triquetrum
Ⓒ   trapezium
Ⓓ   capitate
Ⓔ   hamate

Shoulder dislocation

The stability of the shoulder (glenohumeral) joint depends mainly on surrounding muscles, because the apposing joint surfaces are small, and the ligaments relatively weak. Dislocation of the shoulder is a common injury, particularly when the subject abducts and extends the arm as in throwing the arm back vigorously to catch a ball. The weak ligaments at the front of the glenohumeral joint get torn, and the humeral head pops downwards into the space inferior to the coracoid process and anterior to the glenoid lip. Recurrent dislocation may require surgical repair of the ligaments.

11   *The part of the femur that is palpable at the hip is the:*

Ⓐ   lesser trochanter
Ⓑ   medial condyle
Ⓒ   linea aspera
Ⓓ   greater trochanter
Ⓔ   femoral neck

12   *A prominent feature of the femur immediately superior to the medial condyle is the:*

Ⓐ   greater trochanter
Ⓑ   adductor tubercle
Ⓒ   lesser trochanter
Ⓓ   femoral head
Ⓔ   intercondylar eminence

13   *The proximal end of the tibia is characterised by the presence of:*

Ⓐ   a single articular surface with an eminence laterally
Ⓑ   a dish-shaped articular surface that conforms to the femoral condyles
Ⓒ   paired, flat articular surfaces on either side of an eminence
Ⓓ   paired supracondylar ridges for articulation with the femur
Ⓔ   none of the above is correct

14   *Long bones have internal medullary cavities where:*

Ⓐ   haematopoiesis (blood cell production) takes place
Ⓑ   calcium and phosphate are stored
Ⓒ   immune system surveillance cells predominate
Ⓓ   energy can be stored in the form of yellow fat
Ⓔ   both A and D are correct

Colour and label

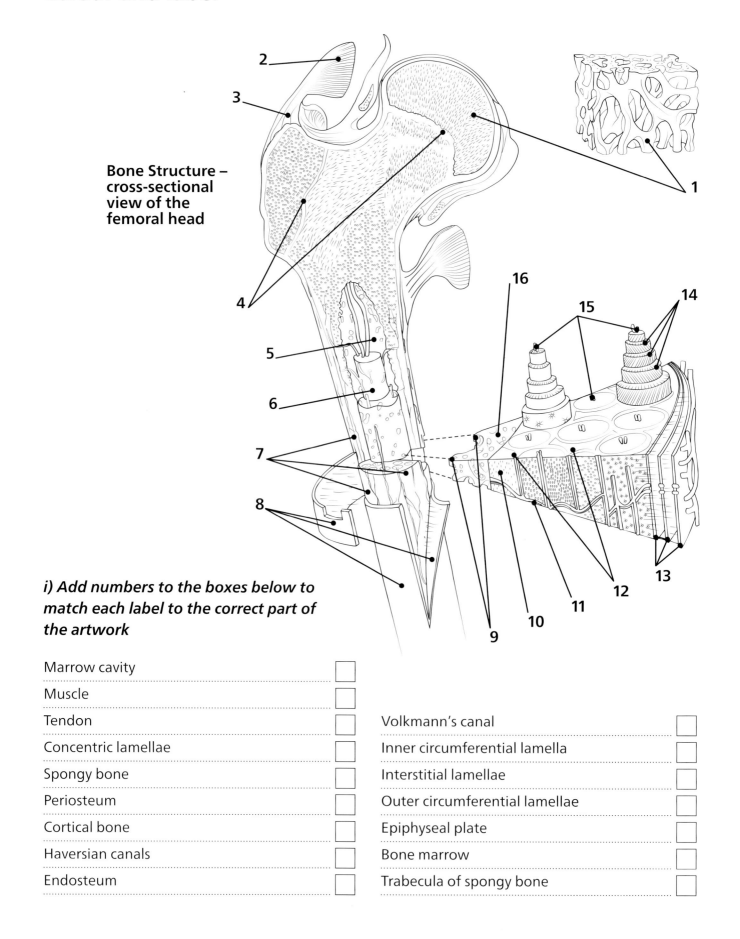

Bone Structure –
cross-sectional
view of the
femoral head

i) Add numbers to the boxes below to
match each label to the correct part of
the artwork

Marrow cavity	☐
Muscle	☐
Tendon	☐
Concentric lamellae	☐
Spongy bone	☐
Periosteum	☐
Cortical bone	☐
Haversian canals	☐
Endosteum	☐

Volkmann's canal	☐
Inner circumferential lamella	☐
Interstitial lamellae	☐
Outer circumferential lamellae	☐
Epiphyseal plate	☐
Bone marrow	☐
Trabecula of spongy bone	☐

i) Label each structure shown on the illustrations

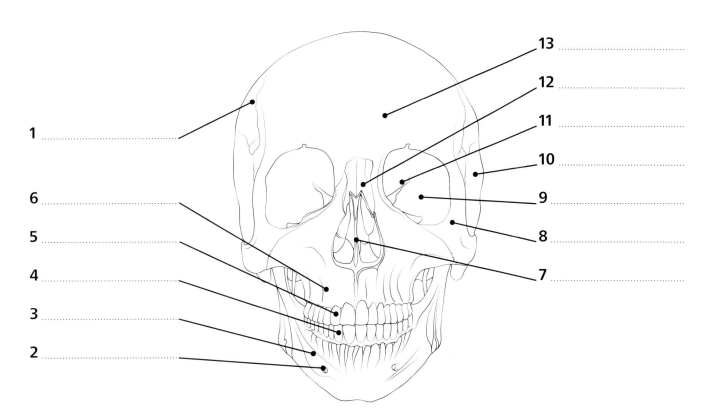

Bones of the Skull – anterior view

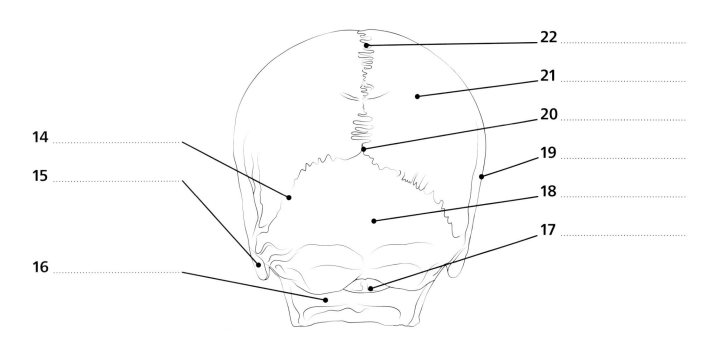

Bones of the Skull – posterior view

Fill in the blanks

1   Vascular supply to the bone tissue is provided by vessels running in the _____, which interconnect the canals of the Haversian system.

2   Longitudinal canals running through the bone tissue and surrounded by concentric lamellae of woven bone are called the _____.

3   The highly sensitive layer of connective tissue on the outside of bone is called the _____.

4   Growth in the circumference of bones occurs by deposition of bone tissue under the _____ on the outside of the bone and by (usually) removal of bone tissue at the _____ of the medullary cavity.

5   The skull is divided into two main regions: _____ and _____.

6   Blood vessels to the bone interior penetrate the surface of the bone through the _____.

7   The vertebral column includes _____ cervical vertebrae, _____ thoracic vertebrae, _____ lumbar vertebrae, _____ fused sacral vertebrae and _____ separate or fused coccygeal vertebrae.

Traumatic neck injury

The cervical vertebral column is the most fragile part of the vertebral column, because it allows the highest degree of mobility. Unfortunately this makes it extremely vulnerable to high acceleration injuries such as blows to the head or motor vehicle accidents. The upper parts of the cervical vertebral column are the most vulnerable, and injuries such as fracture/dislocation of the C1 and C2 vertebrae can have fatal consequences if the cervical spinal cord is severed, and control of respiratory muscles such as the diaphragm is lost. Fractures and dislocation of the lower cervical vertebrae can cause quadriplegia.

8   The _____ provides attachment for muscles of the tongue and protects the airway from collapse.

9   The sacrum has _____ and _____ sacral foramina for the passage of nerve fibres.

10   The proximal end of the humerus has two anterolateral elevations, the _____ and _____, separated by a sulcus.

11 The proximal ulna has a _____ notch to articulate with the humerus.

12 The bones of the digits include _____ and _____ phalanges in digit 1 (the thumb) and _____, _____ and _____ phalanges in digits 2 to 5.

13 The _____ is a space in the hip bone formed by the junction of the superior and inferior rami of the pubic bone with the _____ and _____, respectively.

14 The ischial spine separates the greater and lesser _____ notches.

15 The part of the hip bone palpable at the high side of the hip region is the _____ crest.

16 The _____ is a prominent ridge on the posterior surface of the femur that provides attachment for muscles and intermuscular septa.

17 The space between the two femoral condyles is known as the _____.

18 The _____ is the distal part of the tibia that forms the bony bump on the medial side of the ankle.

19 The navicular bone lies between the _____ and the three _____.

20 The _____ is the bone supported on the calcaneus.

Metacarpophalangeal joint
Carpometacarpal joint
Proximal phalanges
Carpal bones
Proximal interphalangeal joint
Middle phalanx
Capsule
Articular cartilage
Palmar ligament
Distal phalanx
Nail
Proximal phalanx
Distal phalanx of thumb
Distal interphalangeal joint

Bones of the Hand

Each of the four fingers contains three bones, the phalanges, while the thumb contains two phalangeal bones.

Match the statement to the reason

1 Bone microarchitecture is able to resist routine tensile and compressive forces because …

a the cartilaginous epiphyseal growth plates at the ends of long bones are progressively converted into bone during childhood and adolescence.

2 Growth of long bones occurs exclusively before adulthood because…

b progressively lower vertebral bodies must be able to withstand greater compressive forces due to the weight of the trunk, head and upper limbs above them.

3 The sizes of vertebral bodies increase as one descends the vertebral column because …

c the bones of children are more flexible than those of adults.

4 The shaft of the femur is angled inwards towards the knee because …

d the trabeculae or spicules of bone are arranged along the lines of force transmission through the bone for normal weight-bearing function.

5 Children are more prone to greenstick fractures than adults because …

e this keeps the point of contact between the body and the ground as close as possible to the midline during walking, thereby reducing the swaying of the trunk and the energy necessary to balance the body.

1 The ability to breathe deeply declines after the fourth decade of life because …

a this fine balancing reduces the muscular effort of holding the head up when walking upright.

2 The atlas (C1) vertebra lies directly beneath the centre of the skull because …

b much of the blood supply of the femoral head passes through the femoral neck.

3 The cervical lordosis (posterior concavity of the cervical vertebral column) appears only after 3 months of age because …

c the fracture is often due to a fall onto the outstretched hand when one's balance is lost.

4 The femoral head is vulnerable to avascular necrosis following femoral neck fracture because …

d ossification ('turning to bone') of the costal cartilages reduces the flexibility of the chest wall.

5 Fracture of the distal radius is a common injury in the elderly because …

e the infant begins to lift his/her head from that age.

Bone Formation

Bone is continually being formed, enclosing each blood vessel, (a) and (b). As the vessel becomes completely surrounded, and more bone is laid down around it, an osteon is formed (c). The process is continually repeated, resulting in the bone growing in width (d).

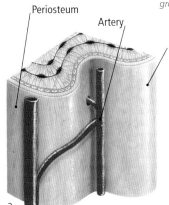

Periosteum
Artery
Ridge

New osteon

a

b

c

d

Colour and label

i) Label each structure shown on the illustrations

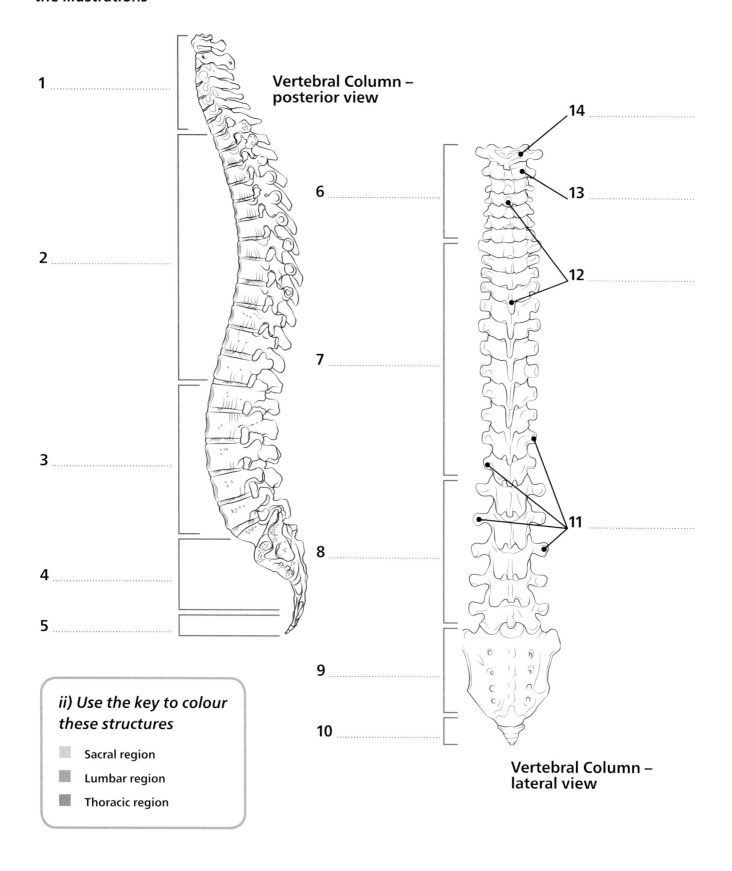

1 ....

2 ....

3 ....

4 ....

5 ....

Vertebral Column – posterior view

6 ....

7 ....

8 ....

9 ....

10 ....

14 ....

13 ....

12 ....

11 ....

Vertebral Column – lateral view

ii) Use the key to colour these structures

Sacral region

Lumbar region

Thoracic region

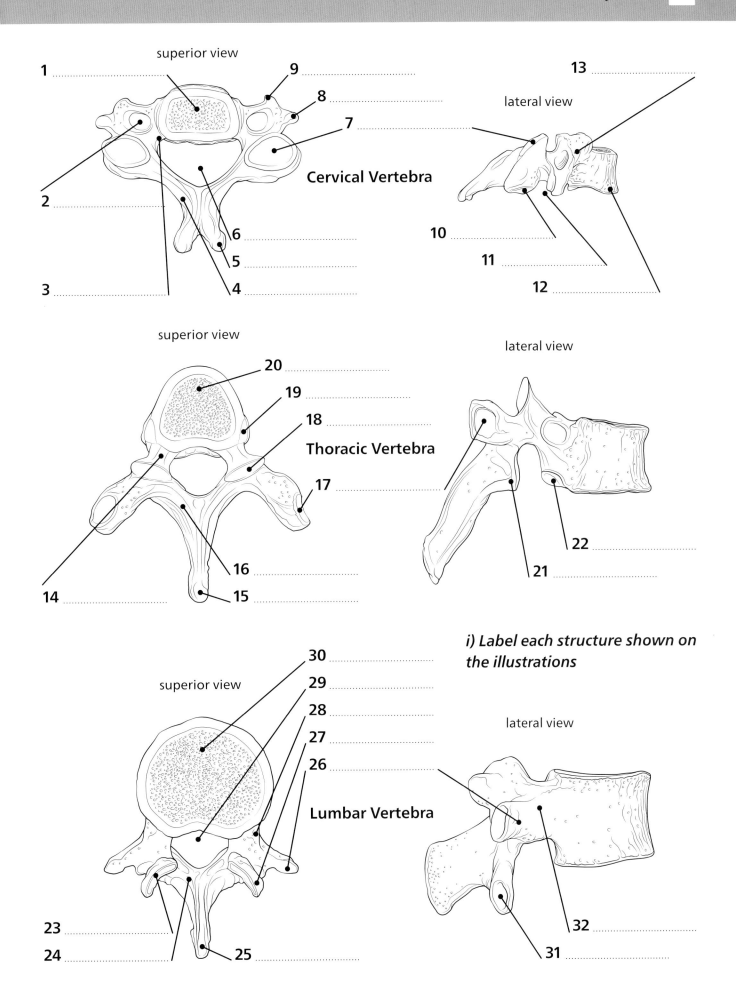

superior view

1 ....

9

8 ....

7 ....

Cervical Vertebra

2 ....

3 ....

6 ....

5 ....

4 ....

13 ....

lateral view

10 ....

11 ....

12 ....

superior view

20 ....

19 ....

18 ....

Thoracic Vertebra

17 ....

16 ....

15 ....

14 ....

lateral view

22 ....

21 ....

i) Label each structure shown on the illustrations

superior view

30 ....

29 ....

28 ....

27 ....

26 ....

Lumbar Vertebra

23 ....

24 ....

25 ....

lateral view

32 ....

31 ....

True or false?

1   The most mechanically stable joints are synovial joints.

2   Examples of fibrous joints would include the sutures of the skull and the gomphoses of the teeth.

3   Ball-and-socket joints are the most mobile in the body, allowing movement around three axes.

4   Ellipsoidal joints, like the radioscaphoid joint in the wrist, allow movement around only one axis.

5   Fibrocartilaginous joints consist of a fibrocartilage disc sandwiched between two joint surfaces.

6   Intervertebral discs consist of a central annulus fibrosus surrounded by a nucleus pulposus.

7   The joint between the trapezium and the base of the first metacarpal is a planar joint.

8   The knee joint is a good example of a hinge joint because it allows only flexion and extension.

9   The joints between the tarsal bones are all essentially planar joints.

10   The ankle joint is formed by the tibia, fibula and talus.

Gliding (Plane) Joint

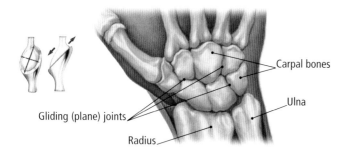

Carpal bones

Ulna

Gliding (plane) joints

Radius

Saddle Joint

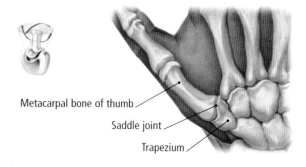

Metacarpal bone of thumb

Saddle joint

Trapezium

Multiple choice

1   *The joint between the scapula and the humerus is highly mobile, but mechanically unstable, because:*

Ⓐ   the glenoid cavity of the scapula is a relatively shallow depression

Ⓑ   there are no bony projections over the superior aspect of the joint

Ⓒ   there are very few muscles providing stability for the joint

Ⓓ   there are no ligaments protecting the joint

Ⓔ   the joint capsule can be easily stripped from the scapula posteriorly

2   *The first carpometacarpal joint (at the base of the thumb) allows which movements?*

Ⓐ   rotation

Ⓑ   inversion

Ⓒ   flexion

Ⓓ   extension

Ⓔ   both C and D are correct

3   *Good example/s of pivot joints would include the:*

Ⓐ   atlantoaxial joint

Ⓑ   proximal and distal radioulnar joints

Ⓒ   thoracic intervertebral joints

Ⓓ   midtarsal joints

Ⓔ   both A and B are correct

4   *Condylar joints are found in the:*

Ⓐ   elbow joint

Ⓑ   ankle joint

Ⓒ   metacarpophalangeal joints

Ⓓ   intercarpal joints

Ⓔ   wrist joint

5   *Stability of the hip joint is maintained by:*

Ⓐ   a ligamentum teres joining the femoral head to the acetabular fossa

Ⓑ   close matching of the acetabular and femoral head surfaces

Ⓒ   strong muscles surrounding the hip joint

Ⓓ   strong iliofemoral, pubofemoral and ischiofemoral ligaments

Ⓔ   all of the above are correct

6   *Stability of the knee joint during standing is achieved by:*

Ⓐ   tension of the surrounding muscles

Ⓑ   strong anterior and posterior longitudinal ligaments

Ⓒ   rotation of the distal femur on the tibia to ensure close-packing of the joint

Ⓓ   tension in the patellar ligament

Ⓔ   none of the above is correct

7   *Interphalangeal joints are examples of which joint type?*

Ⓐ   condylar

Ⓑ   ellipsoidal

Ⓒ   ball and socket

Ⓓ   hinge

Ⓔ   saddle

Ellipsoidal Joint

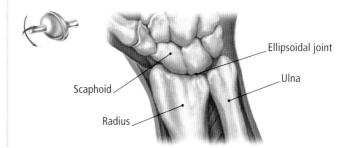

Ellipsoidal joint

Ulna

Scaphoid

Radius

Fill in the blanks

1   Sutures visible on the top (dorsum) of the skull include the _____ and _____ sutures.

2   The joint of the jaw is a bicondylar joint between the _____ of the _____ and the _____ bone.

3   The joint that allows us to shake our heads from side to side is the _____ joint.

4   The joint that allows us to nod our heads is the _____ joint.

5   Joints between vertebrae in the lumbar part of the vertebral column are arranged in a series of _____ planes, so that trunk _____ are possible, but not _____.

6   The paired proximal and distal radio-ulnar joints allow the forearm movements of _____ and _____.

7   The condyloid metacarpophalangeal joints allow the movements of finger _____, _____ and some limited _____.

8   The knee joint allows the movements of _____, _____, _____ and _____.

9   Movements at the midfoot include _____ to turn the sole to face medially and _____ to turn the sole to face laterally.

10   Spraining of the ankle usually involves tearing of the fibres of the _____ and _____ ligaments.

Pivot Joint

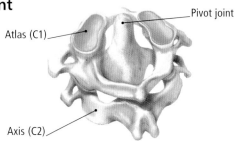

Pivot joint

Atlas (C1)

Axis (C2)

Match the statement to the reason

1 *The fibrous joints of the skull sutures are very mechanically stable because …*

a *the socket of the acetabulum is deep and encircles the femoral head, and strong encircling ligaments stabilise the joint.*

2 *Rotational movements of the trunk mainly occur in the thoracic part of the vertebral column because …*

b *the intervertebral joint planes in that region are aligned on the circumference of a circle centred on the nucleus or core of the intervertebral disc.*

3 *The hip joint is very stable mechanically because …*

c *there is a thin film of lubricating synovial fluid between the articular cartilage surfaces.*

4 *Synovial joints allow free movement of the joint surfaces against each other because …*

d *the glenohumeral ligaments are most easily stripped from the anterior surface of the glenoid lip of the scapula.*

5 *Dislocation of the shoulder usually involves abnormal movement of the humeral head inferiorly and anteriorly because …*

e *the bone edges are locked together by the complex interdigitation of the bone margin.*

Ball-and-socket Joint

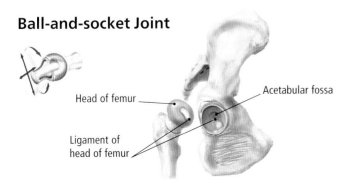

Head of femur

Acetabular fossa

Ligament of head of femur

Hinge Joint

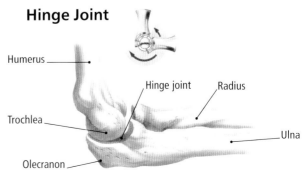

Humerus

Hinge joint

Radius

Trochlea

Ulna

Olecranon

Muscles of the Head, Neck and Trunk

Muscles of the head and neck can be divided into groups concerned with facial movements (muscles of facial expression), moving the eyes (extraocular muscles), chewing (muscles of mastication) and moving the head and neck (cervical muscles). Muscles of the trunk include groups concerned with flexion, extension and rotation of the vertebral column; muscles of lung ventilation (mainly the diaphragm with assistance from intercostal muscles); muscles of the anterolateral abdominal wall; and muscles of the pelvic and urogenital diaphragms.

Key terms:

Deltoid A triangular muscle arising from the lateral clavicle, acromion, and spine of the scapula, and inserting into the deltoid tuberosity of the humerus. It abducts, flexes, or extends the arm depending on which components are activated.

Depressor anguli oris Inserts into the corner of the mouth. It pulls the angle of the mouth downward.

External abdominal oblique The outermost muscle layer of the lateral abdominal wall. When both sides are contracted, they raise intra-abdominal pressure.

Frontalis A sheet-like muscle on the forehead. It attaches to the anterior end of the galea aponeurotica and, by acting alternately with the occipitalis, can move the scalp backward and forward.

Galea aponeurotica A dense, but mobile, connective tissue sheet that supports the scalp.

Iliac crest The large superior ridge of the ilium. It has attachments for the lateral abdominal wall muscles and the quadratus lumborum.

Latissimus dorsi The broadest muscle of the back. It arises from the lower thoracic, lumbar, and sacral vertebrae, and inserts into the humerus. It is a powerful adductor and extensor of the humerus during swimming and climbing.

Levator labii superioris One of the muscles of the mouth. It inserts into the upper lip close to the midline and elevates the upper lip.

Masseter One of the muscles of mastication. It is a quadrilateral muscle that arises from the zygomatic arch and inserts into the ramus of the mandible. It elevates the mandible.

Occipitalis The facial muscle at the back of the scalp that inserts into the galea aponeurotica. When it contracts, it pulls the scalp posteriorly.

Orbicularis oculi A facial muscle that encircles the eye. It closes the eye tightly when it contracts fully.

Orbicularis oris A facial muscle that encircles the lips. It purses or puckers the mouth when it contracts.

Pectoralis major A muscle arising from the medial clavicle and upper six costal cartilages to insert into the crest of the greater tubercle of the humerus. It adducts, medially rotates, and flexes the arm.

Rectus abdominis A long, thin, sheet-like muscle running from the xiphisternum and fifth to seventh costal cartilages to insert into the pubic crest. It flexes the trunk anteriorly.

Serratus anterior Arises from the upper eight ribs and curves around the chest to insert into the medial border of the scapula. It pulls the scapula forward (protraction).

Sternocleidomastoid Extends from the sternoclavicular joint to the mastoid process of the skull. When the two sternocleidomastoids act together, they flex the head on the neck. Acting singly causes rotation of the head to the other side.

Sternohyoid A muscle band from the manubrium of the sternum to the body of the hyoid bone. It lowers the larynx, hyoid, and floor of the mouth.

Temporalis A muscle of mastication (chewing) that arises from the temporal fossa and inserts into the coronoid process and anterior border of the ramus of the mandible. It elevates the mandible.

Teres major Arises from the dorsal scapula near the inferior angle and inserts into the crest of the lesser tubercle of the humerus. It adducts the arm.

Teres minor One of the rotator cuff group. It arises from the dorsal surface of the scapula and inserts into the greater tubercle of the humerus. It laterally rotates the arm.

Thoracolumbar fascia A broad sheet of fascia extending from the vertebral spines of the lower thoracic and lumbar regions to the iliac crest and sacrum. It encloses the latissimus dorsi muscle.

Trapezius Arises from the occipital bone and the cervical and upper thoracic vertebrae. It inserts into the lateral clavicle, and the spine and acromion of the scapula. It elevates and rotates the scapula.

Triceps brachii A three-headed muscle on the posterior aspect of the arm. It arises from the infraglenoid tubercle of the scapula and the back of the humerus, and inserts into the olecranon. It extends the forearm.

Zygomaticus major A muscle band extending from the zygomatic bone of the cheek to the angle of the mouth. It pulls the angle of the mouth laterally.

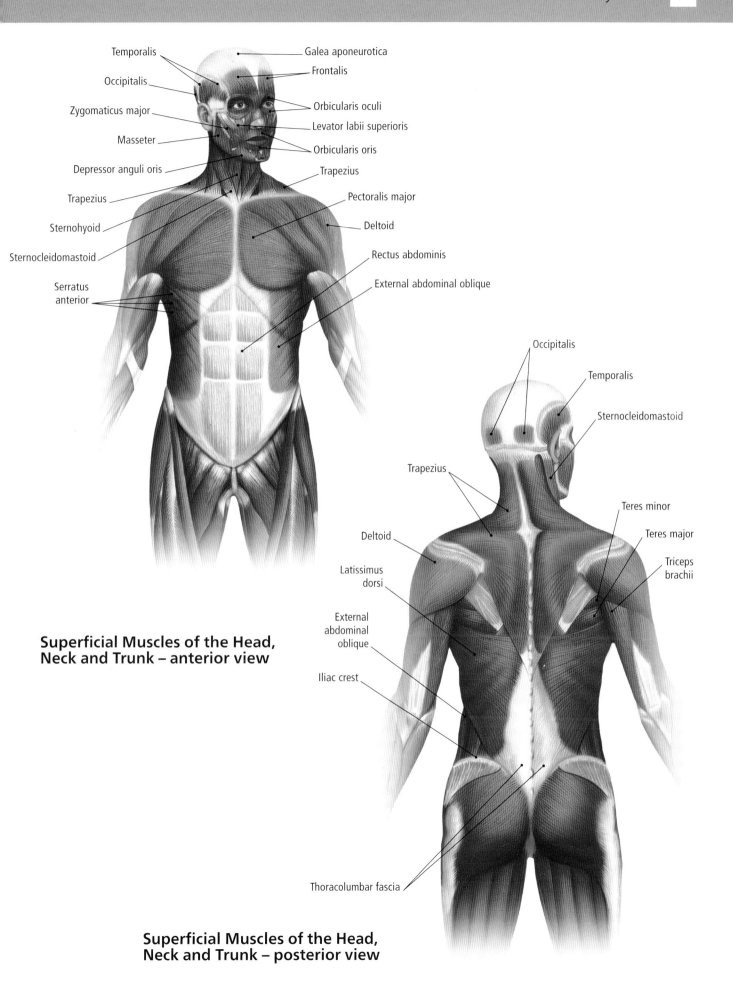

Temporalis

Occipitalis

Zygomaticus major

Masseter

Depressor anguli oris

Trapezius

Sternohyoid

Sternocleidomastoid

Serratus
anterior

Galea aponeurotica

Frontalis

Orbicularis oculi

Levator labii superioris

Orbicularis oris

Trapezius

Pectoralis major

Deltoid

Rectus abdominis

External abdominal oblique

**Superficial Muscles of the Head,
Neck and Trunk – anterior view**

Occipitalis

Temporalis

Sternocleidomastoid

Trapezius

Teres minor

Teres major

Triceps
brachii

Deltoid

Latissimus
dorsi

External
abdominal
oblique

Iliac crest

Thoracolumbar fascia

**Superficial Muscles of the Head,
Neck and Trunk – posterior view**

Muscles of the Upper Limb

Muscles of the upper limb can be divided into muscles of the shoulder girdle (those that move the scapula and humerus), muscles of the arm (mainly biceps brachii, brachialis and triceps brachii), muscles of the forearm (flexor and extensor groups), muscles for forearm rotation, intrinsic muscles of the hand (located in the thenar and hypothenar eminences at the base of the thumb and little finger, respectively), and muscles in the palm.

Key terms:

Abductor pollicis longus Forearm muscle that has a long tendon extending to the first metacarpal. It abducts the thumb.

Anconeus Arises from the lateral epicondyle of the humerus and inserts into the lateral surface of the olecranon. It stabilises the elbow joint during forearm rotation.

Biceps brachii Arises by two heads from the coracoid process and a tubercle immediately above the glenoid cavity (supraglenoid tubercle) and inserts into the forearm at the radial tuberosity and bicipital aponeurosis. It flexes and supinates the forearm.

Brachialis Arises from humerus and inserts into the coronoid process and tuberosity of the ulna. It flexes the forearm.

Brachioradialis Arises from the lateral supracondylar ridge of the humerus and inserts into the lateral surface of the distal radius. It flexes the forearm.

Deltoid See pp. 60–1.

Extensor digiti minimi Arises from the lateral supracondylar ridge of the humerus with a tendon running to the little finger. It allows independent extension of the little finger.

Extensor digitorum Arises from the lateral epicondyle of the humerus and gives rise to multiple tendons, which extend digits 2–5.

Extensor pollicis brevis Arises from the distal radius and inserts into the proximal phalanx of the thumb. It extends the thumb.

Extensor retinaculum A thickening of deep fascia running across the back of the wrist. It holds the extensor tendons to the wrist during the activation of extensor muscles.

Fibrous flexor sheath Fibrous sheaths enclosing the deep and superficial digital flexor tendons. Within these sheaths, the tendons are surrounded by synovial membranes to reduce friction.

Flexor carpi ulnaris Arises from the medial epicondyle of the humerus and inserts into pisiform. It flexes and adducts the hand.

Flexor digitorum superficialis Arises from the medial epicondyle of the humerus. It flexes the middle phalanges of digits 2–5 on the proximal phalanges.

Flexor retinaculum A tough fibrous band running across the wrist, turning the carpal arch into a tunnel. It prevents the bowing of the flexor tendons during activation of the forearm flexor muscles.

Hypothenar muscles Muscles at the base of the little finger. These small muscles abduct or flex the little finger, or oppose it with the thumb.

Lateral head of triceps brachii Arises from the posterior surface of the upper humerus.

Long head of triceps brachii Arises from a tubercle immediately below the glenoid cavity of the scapula.

Palmaris brevis A small muscle that protects the ulnar artery and nerve, and deepens the concavity of the palm when it contracts.

Pectoralis major See pp. 60–1.

Pronator teres Runs from the medial supracondylar ridge of the humerus to the radius. It pronates the forearm.

Tendons of extensors of the digits Inserts into the extensor hoods over the dorsum of each finger and on to the distal phalanges.

Tendon of flexor carpi radialis Inserts into the bases of the second and third metacarpals. It produces flexion and abduction of the hand.

Tendon of flexor carpi ulnaris Inserts into the pisiform bone and exerts its force to other carpal bones by the ligaments between the pisiform and the hamate and fifth metacarpal. It produces flexion and adduction of the hand.

Tendon of palmaris longus Attaches to the flexor retinaculum and the palmar aponeurosis to produce tension in the latter.

Tendon of triceps brachii Inserts into the olecranon to produce extension of the forearm.

Thenar muscles Muscles at the base of the thumb. These muscles flex or abduct the thumb, or oppose it with the other digits.

Triceps brachii A three-headed muscle on the posterior aspect of the arm. It arises from the infraglenoid tubercle of the scapula and the back of the humerus, and inserts into the olecranon. It extends the forearm.

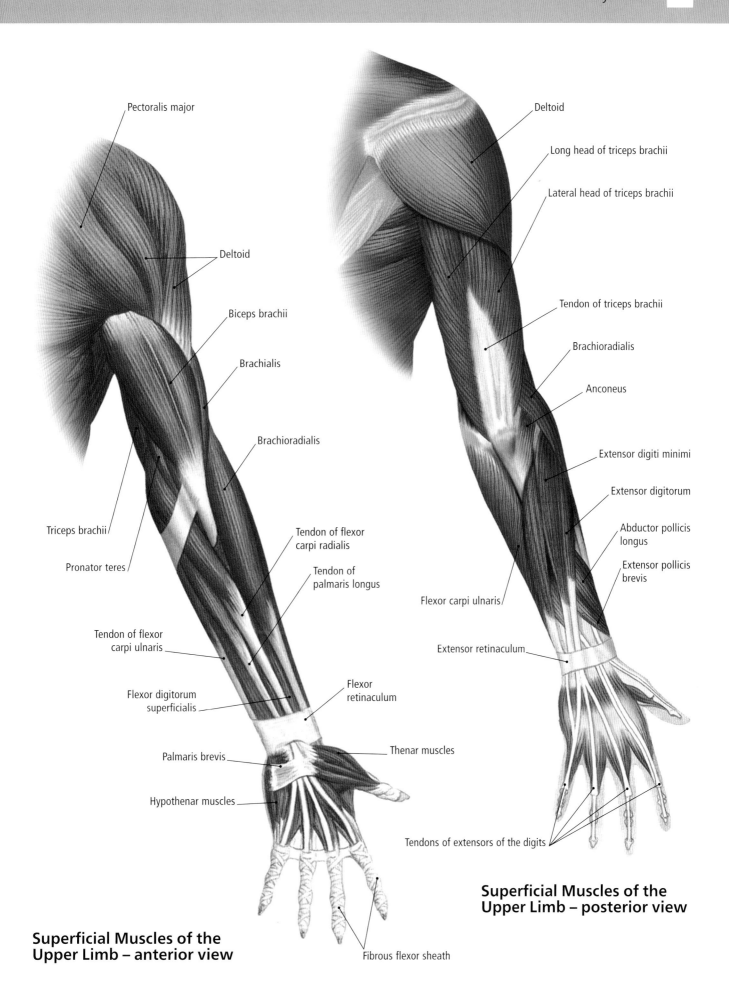

Pectoralis major

Deltoid

Biceps brachii

Brachialis

Brachioradialis

Triceps brachii

Pronator teres

Tendon of flexor carpi ulnaris

Flexor digitorum superficialis

Palmaris brevis

Hypothenar muscles

Tendon of flexor carpi radialis

Tendon of palmaris longus

Flexor retinaculum

Thenar muscles

Fibrous flexor sheath

Deltoid

Long head of triceps brachii

Lateral head of triceps brachii

Tendon of triceps brachii

Brachioradialis

Anconeus

Extensor digiti minimi

Extensor digitorum

Abductor pollicis longus

Extensor pollicis brevis

Flexor carpi ulnaris

Extensor retinaculum

Tendons of extensors of the digits

Superficial Muscles of the Upper Limb – anterior view

Superficial Muscles of the Upper Limb – posterior view

Muscles of the Lower Limb

Muscles of the lower limb are divided into the gluteal or buttock group (mainly for moving the femur laterally and posteriorly); muscle groups of the anterior, medial and posterior thigh (quadriceps femoris, thigh adductors and hamstrings, respectively); muscles of the leg split into anterolateral and posterior groups; and intrinsic muscles of the foot in four layers. Nerves and vessels often run in the connective tissue planes that separate the muscle compartments.

Key terms:

Adductor longus This muscle arises from the body of the pubis and inserts into the medial lip of a ridge on the back of the femur (linea aspera). It adducts the thigh and stabilises it during flexion and extension.

Adductor magnus Has two parts: a large adductor part running from the ischiopubic ramus to the femur, and an extensor part running from the ischial tuberosity to the adductor tubercle of the femur.

Biceps femoris This hamstring muscle has a long head from the ischial tuberosity and a short head from the femur. The common tendon from both heads forms the lateral boundary of the depression behind the knee.

Extensor digitorum longus Runs from the lateral condyle of the tibia and splits into four tendons, which pass under the extensor retinacula of the ankle, before inserting into digits 2–5. It extends the toes.

Fibularis (peroneus) longus Arises from the lateral condyle of the tibia and the fibula. Its tendon crosses under the foot before inserting into the medial cuneiform and base of the first metatarsal. It everts and plantarflexes the foot.

Gastrocnemius A two-headed muscle arising from the femur. The two bellies converge to form a membranous sheet, which fuses with the tendon of the underlying soleus muscle. The gastrocnemius flexes the leg and plantarflexes the foot.

Gluteus maximus This large muscle arises from the ilium, dorsal sacrum, and coccyx. It inserts into the back of the femur and the iliotibial tract of the fascia lata. It is a powerful extensor of the thigh.

Gluteus medius A muscle from the gluteal (posterolateral) surface of the ilium that inserts into the lateral surface of the greater trochanter. It abducts the thigh and supports the pelvis during the stance phase of walking.

Gracilis A slender muscle running from the body of the pubis to the upper medial tibia. It is a flexor, adductor, and medial rotator of the thigh.

Iliopsoas The tendons of the psoas major and iliacus combine to insert into the lesser trochanter of the femur. This combined muscle produces flexion of the thigh.

Iliotibial tract A band of tough connective tissue running from the iliac crest to a sheet of dense connective tissue attached to the side of the patella (lateral retinaculum).

Inferior extensor retinaculum One of two extensor retinacula that hold the extensor tendons in place as they pass anterior and lateral to the ankle joint.

Inguinal ligament A ligament joining the anterior superior iliac spine with the pubic tubercle. It forms the floor of the inguinal canal, which transmits the ductus deferens from the testis.

Lateral head of gastrocnemius Arises from the lateral surface of the lateral condyle of the femur. It may contain a sesamoid bone called the fabella.

Medial head of gastrocnemius Arises from the popliteal surface of the femur and the upper medial condyle of the femur.

Pectineus Arises from the pectineal line of the pubis and inserts into the femur. It adducts the thigh.

Semimembranosus Arises from the ischial tuberosity by a flattened tendon (hence the name) and inserts into the medial tibia. It flexes the leg and extends the thigh.

Semitendinosus Arises in common with the long head of the biceps femoris. Forms a long thin tendon that inserts into the upper medial tibia. Flexes the leg and extends the thigh.

Soleus Arises from the posterior fibula and the posterior intermuscular septum. It receives the tendinous insertion of the gastrocnemius to form a thick strong tendon inserting into the calcaneus. It plantarflexes the foot.

Superior extensor retinaculum One of two extensor retinacula that hold the extensor tendons in place as they pass anterior and lateral to the ankle joint.

Tibialis anterior Arises from the lateral condyle of the tibia and the anterior interosseous membrane, and inserts into the medial cuneiform and base of the first metatarsal. It dorsiflexes and inverts the foot.

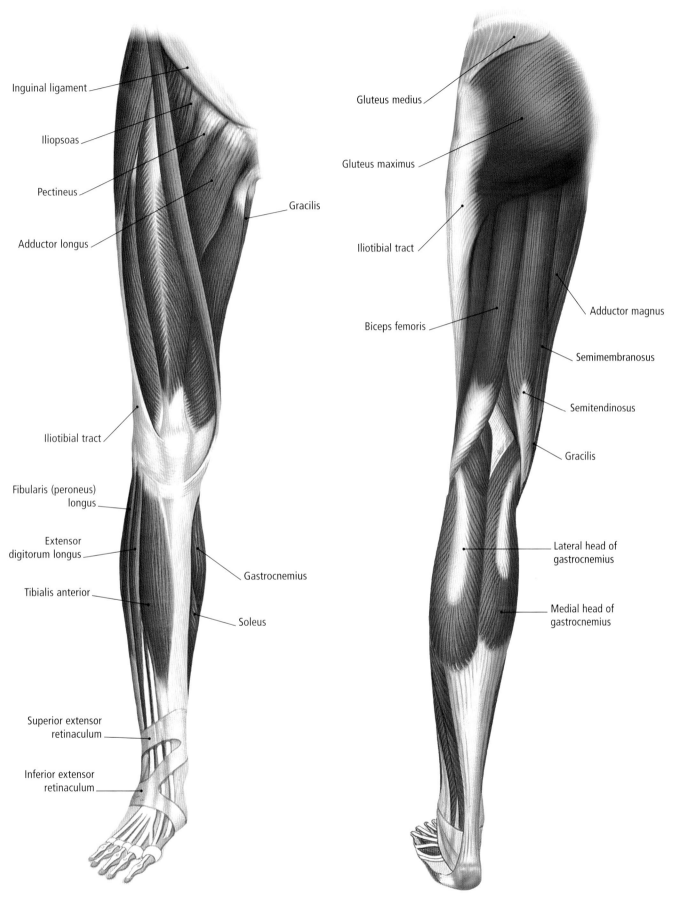

Inguinal ligament

Iliopsoas

Pectineus

Adductor longus

Gracilis

Iliotibial tract

Fibularis (peroneus) longus

Extensor digitorum longus

Tibialis anterior

Gastrocnemius

Soleus

Superior extensor retinaculum

Inferior extensor retinaculum

Gluteus medius

Gluteus maximus

Iliotibial tract

Biceps femoris

Adductor magnus

Semimembranosus

Semitendinosus

Gracilis

Lateral head of gastrocnemius

Medial head of gastrocnemius

**Superficial Muscles of the
Lower Limb – anterior view**

**Superficial Muscles of the
Lower Limb – posterior view**

True or false?

1   *Facial muscles usually have one attachment to bone and the other to subcutaneous tissue.*

2   *Muscle contraction is fundamentally achieved by interactions between the troponin and tropomyosin proteins.*

3   *Digastric muscles are so called because they have two muscle bellies.*

4   *Concentric, circular or sphincteric muscles are usually found surrounding the entrances to body orifices.*

5   *Muscles of the anterolateral abdominal wall are (from outside to inside): transversus abdominis, external oblique and internal oblique.*

6   *In females, the pelvic diaphragm is traversed by the urethra, vagina and anorectal canal.*

7   *The medial fibres of the pelvic diaphragm play a key role in supporting the bladder neck and controlling the onset of urination (micturition).*

8   *The posterior muscles of the rotator cuff group (infraspinatus/teres minor) play a key role in lateral rotation of the humerus.*

9   *The two heads of the biceps brachii attach to the supraglenoid tubercle and coracoid process of the scapula.*

Transverse fibres of extensor expansions (hoods)

Dorsal interosseus muscles

Extensor indicis

Extensor carpi radialis longus

Extensor carpi radialis brevis

Extensor digiti minimi

Extensor pollicis longus

Extensor pollicis brevis

Extensor digitorum

Abductor pollicis longus

Muscles and Tendons of the Hand – dorsal view

Muscles within the hand combine with those of the forearm to enable the fine motor capabilities and dexterity of the hand and fingers.

10   *The triceps brachii attaches to the supraglenoid tubercle of the scapula.*

11   *The role of the biceps brachii muscle is confined to flexion at the elbow.*

12   *The triceps brachii muscle attaches to the coronoid process of the ulna.*

13   *Muscles of the anterior compartment of the forearm are concerned with flexion of the digits and wrist.*

14   *There is a separate extensor indicis muscle that allows the index finger to be independently extended, as in pointing.*

15   *All the intrinsic muscles of the hand are confined to the thenar and hypothenar eminences.*

16   *The principal role of the gluteus maximus is to support the hip when standing on one lower limb.*

17   *Extension of the knee is produced by the quadriceps femoris muscle.*

Thigh muscle injury

Muscles of the thigh, in particular the quadriceps and adductors, are prone to injury from rapid stretching during vigorous sports. Tears of the quadriceps femoris present as sudden pain in the front of the thigh, with swelling and bruising in some cases. Tears of the adductor muscles present as sudden onset of groin pain. Swelling may be present but is so deep that it is often not visible. Strains are usually treated by the principles of protection, rest, ice, compression and elevation (PRICE).

18   *Muscles for everting the foot are located on the lateral side of the leg.*

19   *The gastrocnemius muscles can produce movement only at the ankle joint.*

20   *The muscles of the foot are arranged in five layers.*

Colour and label

i) Label each structure shown on the illustration

Muscle Fibre – microstructure

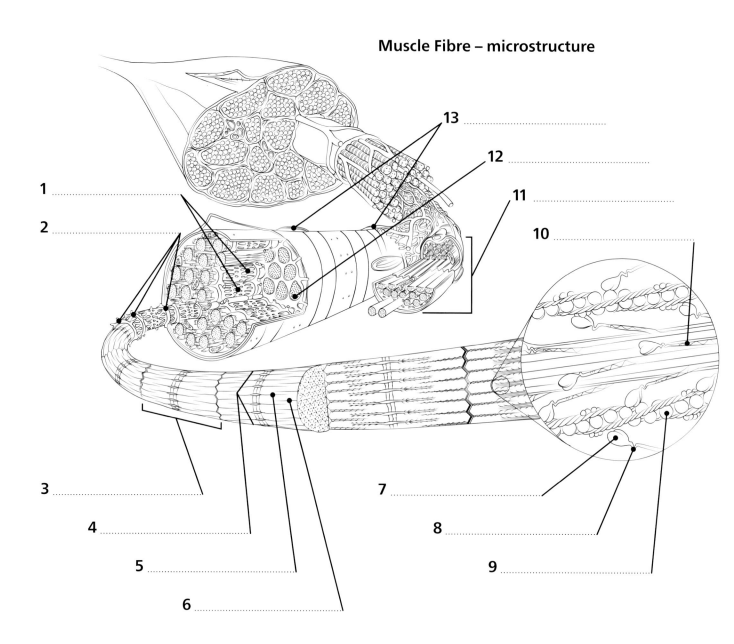

1 ....

2 ....

3 ....

4 ....

5 ....

6 ....

7 ....

8 ....

9 ....

10 ....

11 ....

12 ....

13 ....

Muscle Shapes

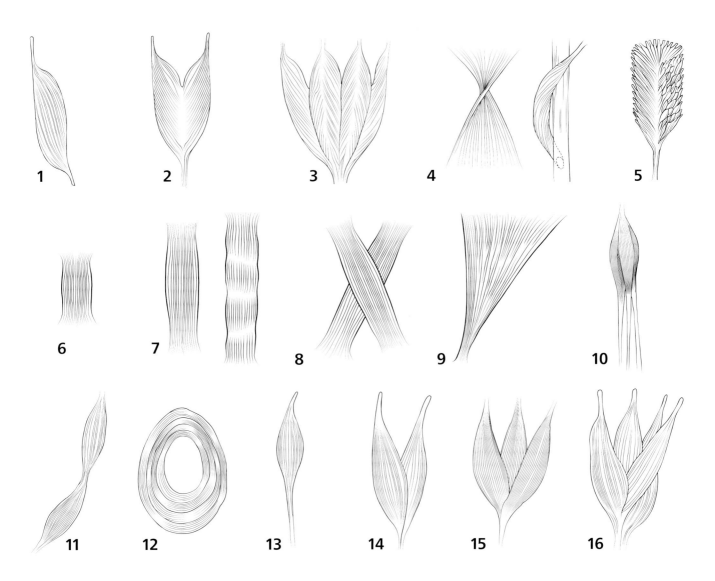

i) Add numbers to the boxes below to match each label to the correct part of the artwork

Multipennate	☐	Multicaudal	☐
Radial	☐	Triangular	☐
Unipennate	☐	Digastric	☐
Quadricipital	☐	Strap	☐
Bipennate	☐	Fusiform	☐
Quadrate	☐	Bicipital	☐
Circular	☐	Tricipital	☐
Cruciate	☐	Spiral	☐

Multiple choice

1   *The role of the T-tubule system of muscle fibres is to:*

(A)   allow the binding of actin and myosin proteins

(B)   take up excess calcium at the end of each contraction

(C)   store elastic potential energy during multiple muscle twitches

(D)   transmit action potentials from the cell surface to the interior

(E)   store acetylcholine for release during end-plate potentials

2   *Which of the following is an example of a multipennate muscle?*

(A)   gracilis

(B)   deltoid

(C)   biceps brachii

(D)   diaphragm

(E)   external oblique

3   *Which architectural feature of a muscle maximises the muscle power for size?*

(A)   large cross-sectional area

(B)   fusiform shape

(C)   cruciate shape

(D)   strap-like shape

(E)   Both A and D are correct

4   *Which of the following muscles can close the mandible during chewing?*

(A)   sternomastoid

(B)   orbicularis oris

(C)   masseter

(D)   zygomaticus major

(E)   zygomaticus minor

5   *Which of the following structures does NOT pass through the diaphragm?*

(A)   descending aorta

(B)   inferior vena cava

(C)   oesophagus

(D)   right phrenic nerve

(E)   portal vein

6   *Which of the following is NOT a function of the anterolateral abdominal muscles?*

(A)   inspiration (breathing in)

(B)   expiration (breathing out)

(C)   trunk rotation to the left

(D)   trunk flexion to the side

(E)   increasing intra-abdominal pressure

7   *Which of the following muscles attaches to the coracoid process of the scapula?*

(A)   triceps brachii

(B)   brachialis

(C)   pectoralis minor

(D)   pectoralis major

(E)   subscapularis

8   *Which muscle is the principal flexor of the elbow?*

(A)   biceps brachii

(B)   coracobrachialis

(C)   pectoralis major

(D)   brachialis

(E)   brachioradialis

9   *Which of the following muscles flexes the distal interphalangeal joints of digits 2 to 5?*

(A)   flexor digitorum superficialis

(B)   flexor digitorum profundus

(C)   flexor carpi ulnaris

(D)   lumbrical muscles

(E)   hypothenar muscles

10 *Flexion at the metacarpophalangeal joints while the interphalangeal and radiocarpal joints are extended requires the:*

(A) adductor pollicis
(B) abductor digiti minimi
(C) interossei
(D) lumbricals
(E) both C and D are correct

11 *Which of the following is NOT a component of the quadriceps femoris muscle?*

(A) vastus intermedius
(B) vastus lateralis
(C) rectus femoris
(D) vastus medialis
(E) gracilis

12 *Which muscle is penetrated by the adductor canal?*

(A) adductor longus
(B) adductor brevis
(C) adductor magnus
(D) semitendinosus
(E) semimembranosus

13 *Which of the following muscles can produce flexion at both the hip and the knee?*

(A) sartorius
(B) gracilis
(C) rectus femoris
(D) adductor magnus
(E) vastus intermedius

14 *Inversion of the foot (turning the sole of the foot to face inwards) is produced mainly by the:*

(A) fibularis (peroneus longus)
(B) extensor digitorum longus
(C) tibialis posterior
(D) flexor digitorum longus
(E) flexor hallucis longus

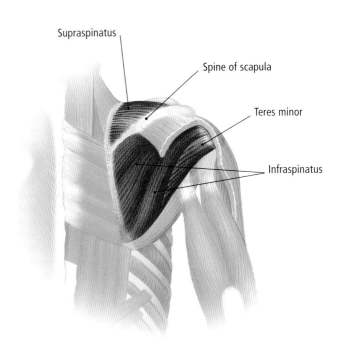

Supraspinatus

Spine of scapula

Teres minor

Infraspinatus

Rotator Cuff Muscles – posterior view

The rotator cuff muscles originate at the scapula (shoulder blade), running across its outer face, and attaching around the head of the humerus.

Rotator cuff and painful arc syndrome

The stability of the shoulder joint is usually maintained by the rotator cuff muscles (supraspinatus, subscapularis, infraspinatus and teres minor). Wear and tear of the supraspinatus tendon due to years of abducting the arm against resistance can cause inflammation of the supraspinatus tendon. This tendon passes through a narrow space beneath the acromion of the scapula, where it can come into contact with hard surfaces during movement. Patients with inflammation of the supraspinatus tendon or adjacent bursa complain of pain when they abduct their arm by more than 60°. When the abduction continues to 120°, the pain is relieved because the humerus rotates under the acromion, and the tendon is no longer compressed. This is known as the painful arc syndrome.

Fill in the blanks

1   Muscles of mastication include the _____, _____, _____, and _____.

2   The sternocleidomastoid muscle produces _____ against resistance when acting bilaterally and turns the head _____ when acting unilaterally.

3   The diaphragm has attachments to three groups of bones: _____, _____ and _____.

4   The pelvic diaphragm has attachments to the _____, _____, _____ and _____ bones.

5   Component muscles of the pelvic diaphragm include the _____, _____, _____ and _____.

6   The two principal muscles used in push-ups are the _____ and _____.

7   Muscles producing pronation of the forearm include the _____ and _____.

8   The biceps brachii muscle can produce the movements of elbow _____, shoulder _____ and forearm _____ thanks to its attachments above the shoulder and below the elbow.

9   The two muscles responsible for supination of the forearm are the _____ and _____.

10   Precision grip mainly depends on the actions of the _____ muscles of the hand.

11   The power grip is achieved mainly by application of the _____ muscles of the forearm.

12   *Muscles of the _____ group are critically important for the ability to support the body weight on one leg during the stance phase of walking.*

13   *The thigh muscles are arranged in three groups: quadriceps femoris, _____ and _____ .*

14   *The _____ provides attachment for the hamstrings and adductor magnus.*

15   *The only muscle of the quadriceps femoris group that crosses two joints is the _____ .*

16   *Muscles of the hamstring group include the _____ , _____ and _____ .*

17   *External or lateral rotators of the hip include the _____ , _____ , _____ and _____ femoris.*

18   *Muscles of the adductor group of the thigh include the _____ , _____ , _____ , _____ , _____ and _____ .*

Pelvic Floor Muscles (Female) – anterior view

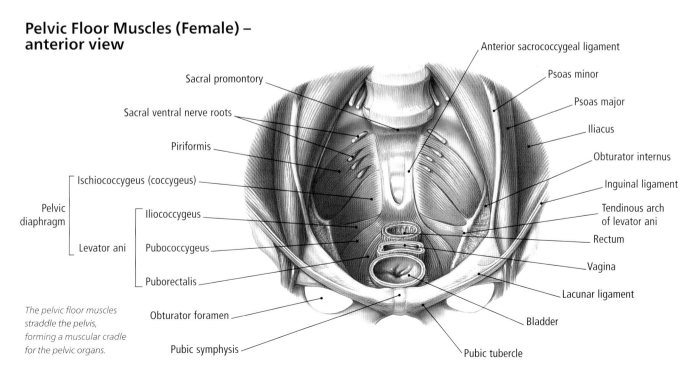

Anterior sacrococcygeal ligament
Psoas minor
Psoas major
Iliacus
Obturator internus
Inguinal ligament
Tendinous arch of levator ani
Rectum
Vagina
Lacunar ligament
Bladder
Pubic tubercle
Pubic symphysis
Obturator foramen
Puborectalis
Pubococcygeus
Iliococcygeus
Ischiococcygeus (coccygeus)
Piriformis
Sacral ventral nerve roots
Sacral promontory
Pelvic diaphragm
Levator ani

The pelvic floor muscles straddle the pelvis, forming a muscular cradle for the pelvic organs.

Colour and label

**Superficial and
Deep Muscles of
the Head and Neck –
anterior view**

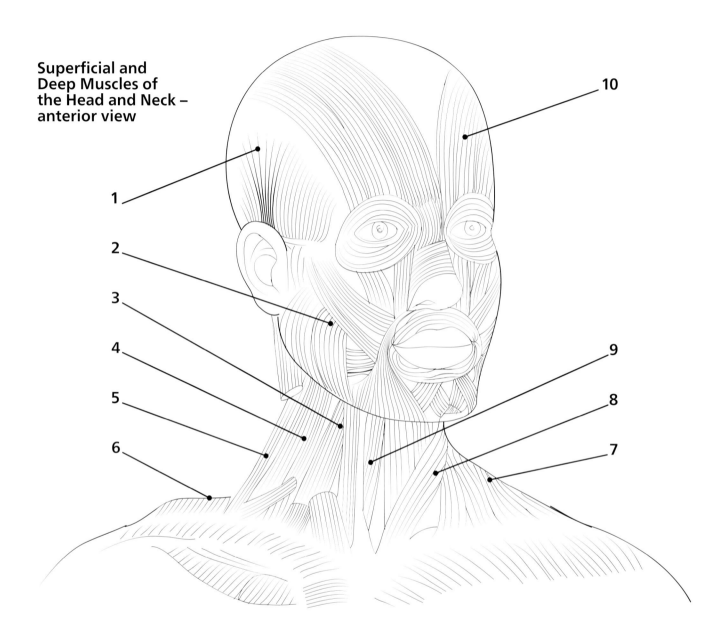

i) Add numbers to the boxes below to match each label to the correct part of the artwork

Scalenus medius	☐	Trapezius (cut)	☐
Frontalis	☐	Temporalis	☐
Scalenus anterior	☐	Trapezius	☐
Sternocleidomastoid	☐	Sternohyoid	☐
Levator scapulae	☐	Masseter	☐

i) Label each structure shown on the illustration

ii) Colour the trapezius red and the latissimus dorsi orange

Superficial Muscles of the Back – posterior view

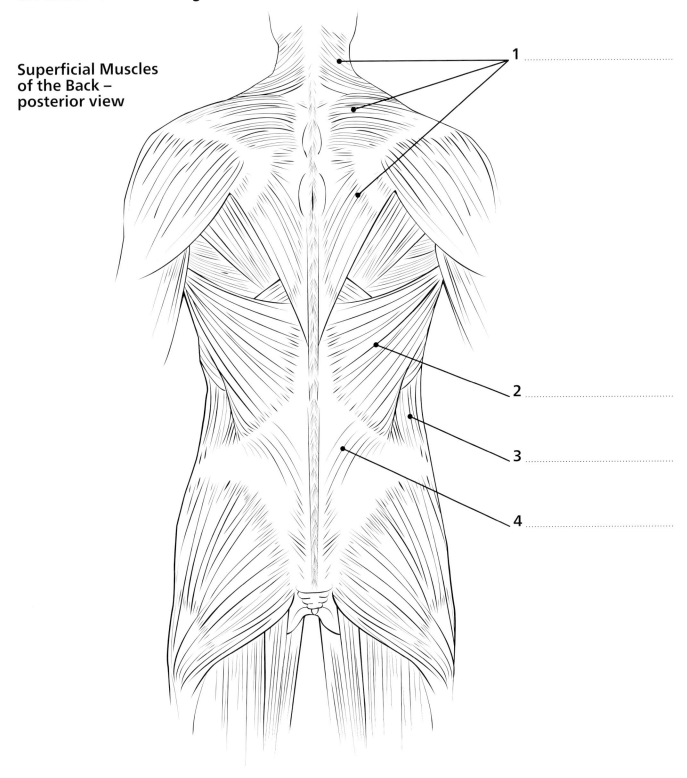

1 ....

2 ....

3 ....

4 ....

Match the statement to the reason

1   The biceps brachii muscle is able to produce supination of the forearm because …

a   the medial and lateral gastrocnemius attach to the femur above the knee joint, and all three muscles (the two gastrocnemius and the soleus) insert onto the calcaneus below the ankle joint.

2   The fibres of the vastus medialis (quadriceps femoris group) approach the patella obliquely because …

b   the almost horizontal orientation of these muscle fibres allows them to stabilise the patella against the intercondylar surface of the distal femur.

3   The triceps surae group is able to produce both plantar flexion and flexion of the knee, because …

c   when the forearm is in the anatomical position, the bicipital tendon curves around the radius to insert onto the radial tuberosity.

Muscles of the Neck – transverse section

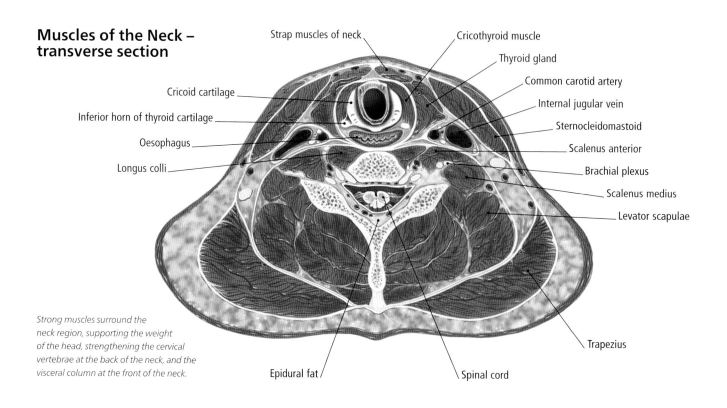

Strap muscles of neck
Cricothyroid muscle
Thyroid gland
Cricoid cartilage
Inferior horn of thyroid cartilage
Common carotid artery
Internal jugular vein
Oesophagus
Sternocleidomastoid
Longus colli
Scalenus anterior
Brachial plexus
Scalenus medius
Levator scapulae
Trapezius
Epidural fat
Spinal cord

Strong muscles surround the neck region, supporting the weight of the head, strengthening the cervical vertebrae at the back of the neck, and the visceral column at the front of the neck.

1 *The neck muscles of modern humans are relatively weak compared with our nearest relatives because …*

a *the medial fibres of the pelvic diaphragm (levator prostatae) in males and pubovaginalis in females support the urinary bladder neck and regulate initiation of bladder emptying.*

2 *The diaphragm assists with the return of venous blood from the lower body to the heart because …*

b *it is a powerful hip extensor.*

3 *Pelvic diaphragm exercises are important to maintain urinary continence because …*

c *modern humans rely on balancing of the skull more than muscular effort to keep the head stable.*

4 *The gluteus maximus is an important muscle for climbing stairs because …*

d *it is a powerful adductor and extensor of the humerus when the arm is above the head.*

5 *The latissimus dorsi is well developed in freestyle swimmers because …*

e *it compresses the abdomen, raising pressure in the abdomen above that in the thorax.*

Muscles of ventilation and lung disease

Most of the muscular effort required for normal lung ventilation is during inspiration (breathing in) because the elastic potential energy built up during inspiration can be harnessed to force air out of the lungs. The main muscle of inspiration is the diaphragm, which increases the vertical dimension of the chest when it contracts. Additional inspiratory force is applied by the external intercostal muscles and by those shoulder girdle muscles that have attachment to the ribs (pectoralis major and minor, and serratus anterior). Use of the latter is seen in chronic obstructive pulmonary disease, where the patient struggles to draw air into the lungs. Patients struggling to breathe out, for example in asthma, will make use of the anterolateral abdominal wall muscles.

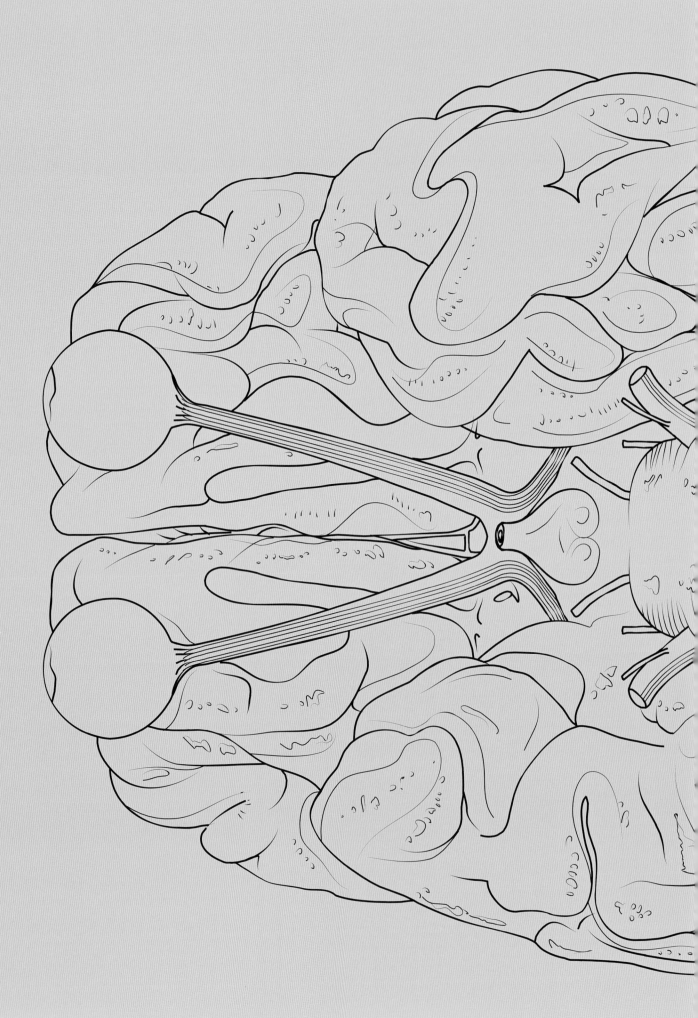

CHAPTER 3: THE NERVOUS SYSTEM

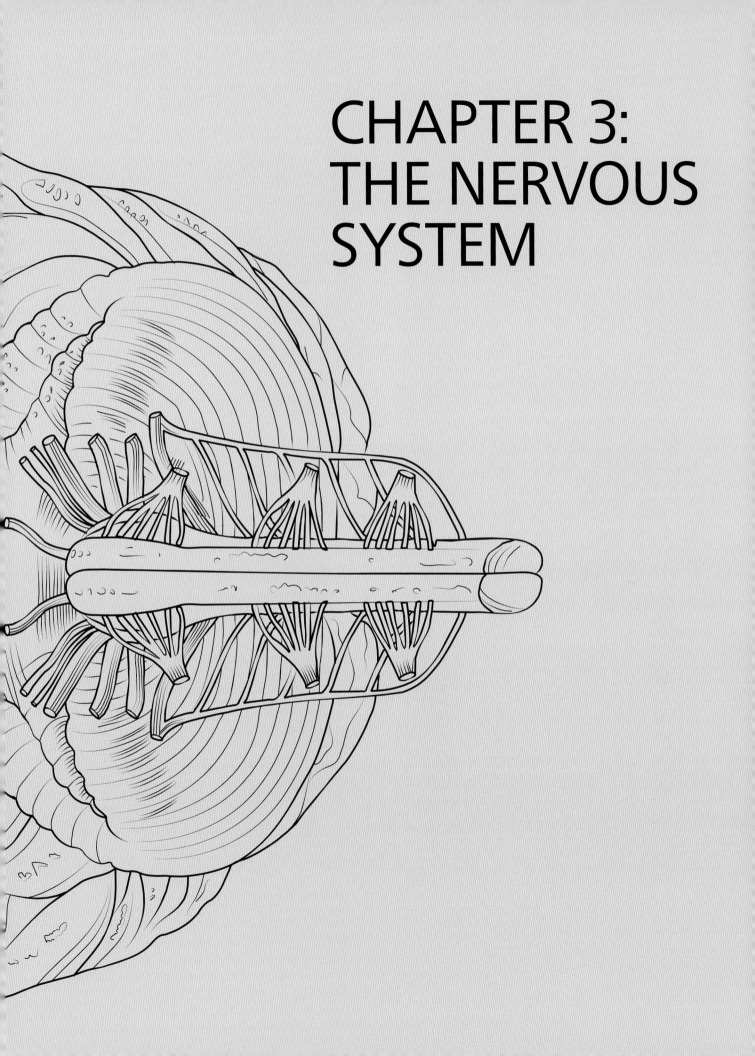

The Peripheral Nervous System

The peripheral nervous system is that part of the nervous system outside the brain and spinal cord. It includes groups of nerve cell bodies (ganglia) and the peripheral nerves. Ganglia may be sensory in function, e.g. the cranial nerve sensory ganglia and the spinal or dorsal root ganglia, or they may be autonomic (part of the sympathetic or parasympathetic nervous systems). There is also a nerve network within the gut tube (enteric nervous system).

Key terms:

Axillary (circumflex) nerve One of the branches of the brachial plexus, supplies the deltoid and teres minor muscles, shoulder joint, and skin on the back of the arm.

Brachial plexus A network of nerves formed from spinal nerves cervical 5 to thoracic 1 to supply the upper limb. Major nerves arising from it are the radial, ulnar, median, axillary (circumflex), and musculocutaneous.

Cauda equina The roots of the lumbar, sacral, and coccygeal nerves in the vertebral canal beyond the end of the spinal cord. The name derives from the similarity to a horse's tail.

Cervical enlargement of spinal cord Enlargement of the spinal cord at spinal segments cervical 5 to thoracic 1. It supplies the upper limb and houses the neurons concerned with sensory input from, and motor control of, that limb.

Cervical nerve Branches of the cervical plexus supply muscles of the neck and skin of the neck and posterior head.

Common fibular nerve Branch of the sciatic nerve, descends through the popliteal fossa to the neck of the fibula, and branches into deep and superficial fibular nerves.

Deep fibular nerve Supplies the tibialis anterior, extensor hallucis longus, extensor digitorum longus, and fibularis (peroneus) tertius muscles, as well as the tarsal joints and dorsal skin of the first and second toes.

Digital nerve Runs along either side of a digit (hand or foot), supplying sensation to that side.

Femoral nerve The largest branch of the lumbar plexus, emerges behind the psoas major and passes deep to the inguinal ligament to enter the femoral triangle at the front of the thigh. Supplies the quadriceps femoris, pectineus, sartorius, and iliopsoas, as well as the skin of the front of the thigh and anteromedial leg.

Intercostal nerve Runs in the space between adjacent ribs. Upper intercostal nerves supply the intercostal muscles and skin of the chest. Lower intercostal nerves cross into the abdomen (thoraco-abdominal nerves) to supply abdominal muscles and the skin of the abdomen.

Lateral femoral cutaneous nerve Branch of the lumbar plexus, supplies the skin of the lateral surface of the thigh.

Lumbosacral enlargement of spinal cord Enlargement of the spinal cord at spinal segments lumbar 2 to sacral 3. The enlargement houses neurons controlling muscles, or processing information from the skin, of the lower limb.

Lumbosacral plexus Network of nerves formed from spinal nerves lumbar 2 to sacral 3 to supply the lower limb and perineum. Can be divided into a lumbar plexus on posterior abdominal wall and a sacral plexus in the pelvic cavity.

Median nerve Branch of the brachial plexus, supplies all muscles of the front of the forearm except flexor carpi ulnaris and the medial half of the deep flexors of the fingers. Also supplies the thumb muscles and the skin of the lateral palm and digits.

Medulla oblongata The lowest part of the brainstem. It connects the spinal cord with the pons.

Musculocutaneous nerve Branch of the brachial plexus, supplies the biceps brachii muscle and skin of the forearm.

Obturator nerve Branch of the lower lumbar plexus, supplies the adductor group of thigh muscles and the skin of the upper medial thigh.

Radial nerve Branch of the brachial plexus, supplies the triceps brachii, anconeus, brachioradialis, and muscles of the extensor compartment of the forearm. Also supplies the skin of the lateral dorsum of the hand.

Sciatic nerve This branch of the sacral plexus is the largest nerve in the body. It divides into tibial and common fibular nerves, which supply the muscles of the posterior thigh and all of the leg and foot.

Superficial fibular nerve Branch of the common fibular nerve, supplies the fibularis (peroneus) longus and brevis muscles, and the skin of the lateral leg and dorsum of the foot and toes.

Sural nerve A cutaneous branch of the tibial nerve, supplies the back of the calf, the foot, and heel.

Tibial nerve Branch of the sciatic nerve, passes through the popliteal fossa to give muscular branches to soleus, tibialis posterior, flexor hallucis longus and flexor digitorum longus.

Ulnar nerve A branch of the brachial plexus, supplies the flexor carpi ulnaris, medial flexor digitorum profundus, muscles of the little finger, interosseus muscles of the palm, the adductor pollicis muscles, and the skin of the medial one-and-a-half digits.

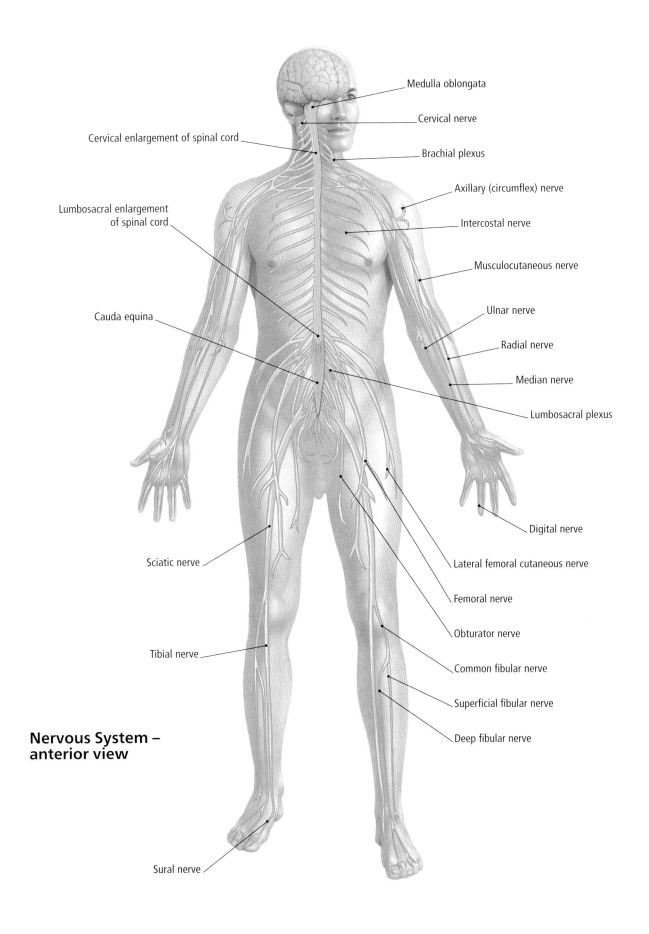

Medulla oblongata

Cervical nerve

Cervical enlargement of spinal cord

Brachial plexus

Axillary (circumflex) nerve

Lumbosacral enlargement of spinal cord

Intercostal nerve

Musculocutaneous nerve

Cauda equina

Ulnar nerve

Radial nerve

Median nerve

Lumbosacral plexus

Digital nerve

Sciatic nerve

Lateral femoral cutaneous nerve

Femoral nerve

Tibial nerve

Obturator nerve

Common fibular nerve

Superficial fibular nerve

Deep fibular nerve

Nervous System – anterior view

Sural nerve

The Spinal Cord

The spinal cord is that part of the central nervous system that lies within the vertebral column. It connects with the brain above and has more than 32 pairs of spinal nerves attached. The spinal cord has dorsal and ventral roots attached to its posterolateral and anterolateral margins, respectively. The dorsal roots carry sensory information from the skin, limbs, body wall and internal organs, whereas the ventral roots carry motor and autonomic commands to muscles and glands.

Key terms:

Anterior corticospinal tract Descending spinal cord pathway from cerebral cortex to almost all levels of the spinal cord.

Anterior median fissure A deep groove in the front of the spinal cord.

Anterior radicular artery A fine artery that runs along and supplies the ventral rootlets of the spinal cord.

Anterior ramus of spinal nerve Branch of the spinal nerve. Supplies muscles, bones, joints, and skin of the limbs and anterolateral body wall, and organs of ventral body cavities.

Anterior spinal artery An artery running longitudinally in the anterior median fissure of the spinal cord.

Anterior spinal vein A vein running longitudinally in the anterior median fissure of the spinal cord.

Arachnoid The delicate spider's web-like membrane underlying the dura mater.

Axon The long process of a nerve cell that transmits the impulse to another part of the brain or body.

Central canal A delicate fluid-filled tube in the centre of the spinal cord.

Cuneate fasciculus Bundle of ascending axons carrying info about discriminative touch, vibration, and conscious proprioception from upper trunk and limbs to the medulla.

Dorsal funiculus The region of white matter on the dorsal or posterior aspect of the spinal cord.

Dorsal horn The region of the spinal cord grey matter concerned with sensory input.

Dorsal rootlets Fine nerve fibres carrying sensory information from the skin surface, muscles, and internal organs.

Dorsal spinocerebellar tract Spinal cord pathway carrying non-conscious proprioceptive information from the upper spinal cord to the cerebellum.

Dorsolateral sulcus A groove running longitudinally down the posterolateral surface of the spinal cord.

Dura mater The tough outer layer of the meninges.

Endoneurium Delicate connective tissue holding together the individual nerve fibres in a fascicle (fine nerve bundle).

Epineurium The connective tissue sheath around an entire spinal nerve or trunk.

Gracile fasciculus Bundle of ascending axons carrying info about discriminative touch, vibration, and conscious proprioception from lower trunk and limbs to medulla.

Grey ramus communicans A nerve strand joining the sympathetic trunk to the spinal nerve.

Lateral corticospinal tract A descending spinal cord pathway from the cerebral cortex to almost all levels of the spinal cord.

Lateral funiculus The region of white matter on the lateral aspect of the spinal cord.

Lateral reticulospinal tract A descending spinal cord pathway from the reticular formation of the brainstem to the spinal cord.

Lateral vestibulospinal tract A descending spinal cord pathway from the lateral vestibular nucleus of the brain stem to all levels of the spinal cord.

Medial reticulospinal tract A descending spinal cord pathway from the reticular formation of the brainstem to the spinal cord.

Medial vestibulospinal tract A descending spinal cord pathway from the vestibular nuclei of the brainstem to the cervical levels of the spinal cord.

Myelin sheath of Schwann cell Each Schwann cell wraps its cytoplasm around a peripheral axon to form one internodal segment of the myelin sheath.

Node of Ranvier The region of a myelinated nerve fibre where the axon is naked.

Perineurium The connective tissue sheath around a fascicle or primary bundle of nerve fibres.

Pia mater The most delicate layer of the meninges, it is in direct contact with the brain surface.

Posterior radicular artery An arterial branch that runs along and supplies the dorsal or posterior roots of the spinal cord.

Posterior ramus of spinal nerve A branch of the spinal nerve that supplies the muscles, bones, joints, and skin of the back.

Posterior spinal artery One of a pair of arteries running longitudinally along the grooves of the spinal cord where the dorsal roots attach.

Posterior spinal vein A vein running longitudinally along the posterior median fissure of the spinal cord.

Spinal Cord – cross-sectional view

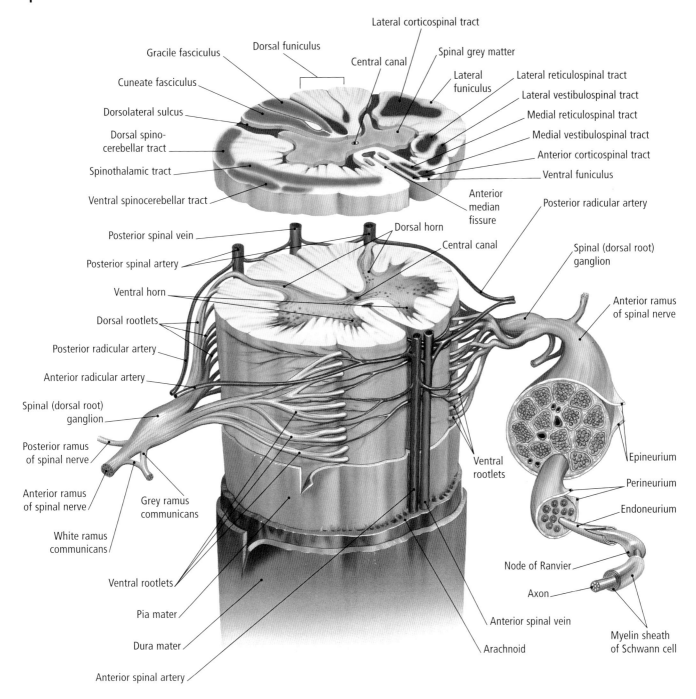

Spinal (dorsal root) ganglion A collection of sensory neurons lying along the dorsal root.

Spinal grey matter An 'H'-shaped region in the centre of the spinal cord.

Spinothalamic tract A spinal cord pathway that carries information about pain, temperature, and simple touch from all levels of the spinal cord to the thalamus.

Ventral funiculus The region of white matter on the ventral or anterior aspect of the spinal cord.

Ventral horn The region of the spinal cord grey matter where the cell bodies of motor neurons and their associated interneurons are located.

Ventral rootlets Fine nerve fibres carrying motor neuron axons from the ventral surface of the spinal cord to the spinal nerve.

Ventral spinocerebellar tract A spinal cord pathway carrying non-conscious proprioceptive information from the lower spinal cord to the cerebellum.

White ramus communicans A nerve strand joining the sympathetic ganglia to the spinal nerve.

True or false?

1   *The ascending and descending pathways within the spinal cord are located within the grey matter.*

2   *The dorsal horn of the spinal cord contains neurons concerned with sensory function from the skin, muscles and joints.*

3   *The ventral roots of the spinal cord contain outgoing (efferent) axons of skeletal muscle motor neurons and preganglionic visceral autonomic neurons.*

4   *The dorsal root ganglion cells are autonomic visceromotor in function.*

5   *Blood supply to the spinal cord is provided by a single midline anterior spinal artery and paired posterior spinal arteries.*

6   *The radial nerve supplies the triceps brachii and the forearm extensor compartment muscles.*

7   *The largest nerve in the body is the femoral nerve that supplies the quadriceps femoris muscle.*

8   *The median nerve passes through the carpal tunnel in the wrist, where it can be compressed in carpal tunnel syndrome.*

9   *The ulnar nerve is vulnerable to damage where it runs posterior to the lateral epicondyle.*

10   *The sciatic nerve divides into the posterior tibial and common peroneal (fibular) nerves.*

Multiple choice

1 *Which of the following tissues or cell types would NOT be found inside the spinal cord?*

Ⓐ choroid plexus
Ⓑ microglia
Ⓒ astrocyte
Ⓓ oligodendrocyte
Ⓔ vascular endothelial cell

2 *Where are the autonomic preganglionic neurons located?*

Ⓐ the dorsal horn
Ⓑ the ventral horn
Ⓒ the lateral horn
Ⓓ the white matter
Ⓔ the ganglia of the abdominal cavity

3 *Concerning the human spinal nerves, there are:*

Ⓐ 7 cervical, 12 thoracic, 5 lumbar and 5 sacral
Ⓑ 8 cervical, 11 thoracic, 5 lumbar and 5 sacral
Ⓒ 8 cervical, 12 thoracic, 5 lumbar and 5 sacral
Ⓓ 8 cervical, 12 thoracic, 4 lumbar and 5 sacral
Ⓔ 7 cervical, 11 thoracic, 5 lumbar and 5 sacral

4 *Which of the following muscles are supplied by the median nerve?*

Ⓐ biceps brachii
Ⓑ short muscles of the thumb (thenar eminence)
Ⓒ brachioradialis
Ⓓ extensors of the wrist
Ⓔ muscles of the little finger (hypothenar eminence)

5 *Where is the radial nerve most likely to be damaged?*

Ⓐ on the dorsum of the wrist at the base of the thumb
Ⓑ in the cubital fossa near the brachial artery
Ⓒ in the medial forearm near the flexor digiti minimi
Ⓓ as it passes posterior to the middle part of the humerus
Ⓔ in the axilla against the teres major tendon

6 *Where is the femoral nerve closest to the skin surface?*

Ⓐ in the femoral triangle
Ⓑ immediately above the adductor tubercle of the femur
Ⓒ as it passes anterior to the iliacus
Ⓓ near the anterior superior iliac spine
Ⓔ deep to the gluteus medius

7 *Which of the following muscles is/are supplied by the sciatic nerve?*

Ⓐ gluteus maximus
Ⓑ adductor magnus
Ⓒ semitendinosus
Ⓓ biceps femoris
Ⓔ both C and D are correct

Neuron

The unique structure of neurons comprises several dendrites and a single axon projecting from the cell body. Nerve impulses are received by the dendrites and carried to the cell body, while the axon carries impulses away from the cell body.

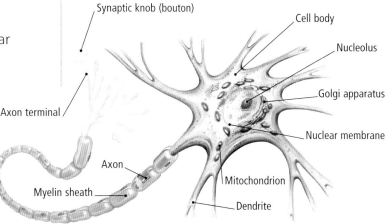

Synaptic knob (bouton)
Cell body
Nucleolus
Golgi apparatus
Axon terminal
Nuclear membrane
Axon
Mitochondrion
Myelin sheath
Dendrite

Fill in the blanks

1   The _____ of the spinal cord is a fluid-filled remnant of the embryonic neural tube.

2   The _____ of the spinal cord contains the nerve cell bodies and most of their dendritic processes.

3   The brachial plexus for nerve supply to the upper limb is derived usually from the _____ to _____ spinal nerves, inclusive.

4   The axillary (circumflex) nerve supplies the _____ muscle and a patch of skin over the _____.

5   The biceps brachii and brachialis muscles are supplied by the _____ nerve.

6   The sympathetic outflow from the central nervous system is through the _____ to _____ spinal nerves.

Paraplegia

Paraplegia is the result of spinal cord injury between the T1 and L2 vertebrae. It results in loss of movement in parts of the body below the injured area.

T1

Spinal cord

L1

L2

Spine

7   The parasympathetic supply to the pelvic organs is through the _____ nerves.

8   The _____ nerve supplies the adductor muscles of the thigh.

9   Sensory supply to the medial side of the leg is by the _____ nerve, a branch of the _____ nerve.

10 All the intrinsic muscles of the foot are supplied by branches of the _____ nerve, which is in turn a branch of the _____ nerve.

Match the statement to the reason

1   *Damage to the wall of the descending aorta can cause an infarct (death of tissue) of the caudal segments of the spinal cord because …*

a   *the sciatic nerve runs in the medial and inferior quadrants of the buttock and can be damaged by injection there.*

2   *Fractures of the midshaft of the radius can cause wrist drop because …*

b   *the radial nerve that passes posterior to the humeral shaft supplies the extensors of the wrist.*

3   *Injections into the gluteus maximus of the buttock should always be made into the centre of the superior and lateral quadrant because …*

c   *the median nerve that supplies the thenar muscles and skin of the lateral palm passes anterior to the distal humerus.*

4   *Fractures of the distal humerus can cause paralysis of thumb movement and loss of sensation over the lateral palm because …*

d   *arterial supply to the lumbosacral spinal cord is derived from the abdominal aorta.*

Paraplegia

Damage to the spinal cord below the T1 segmental level will lead to paralysis of only the trunk and two lower limbs (paraplegia) as well as loss of direct cortical control of bowel and urinary bladder function. If the site of injury is large, all ascending and descending transfer of information will be blocked. Spinal cord damage may be congenital, for example, spina bifida, or due to injury sustained through motor vehicle or sporting accident, gunshot or knife wound. Muscles of the affected limbs will develop spastic paralysis, where muscle tone and reflexes are increased.

Colour and label

Major Nerves of the Wrist – palmar view

Major Nerves of the Upper Limb – anterior view

Major Nerves of the Upper Limb – posterior view

9

10
11
12
13
14
15

1
2
3
4
8
7
5
6

i) Add numbers to the boxes below to match each label to the correct part of the artwork

Radial nerve ☐

Axillary nerve ☐

Median nerve ☐

Flexor retinaculum ☐

Anterior interosseus nerve ☐

Digital nerves of radial nerve ☐

Superficial branch of radial nerve ☐

Median nerve ☐

Ulnar nerve ☐

Common palmar digital branches of median nerve ☐

Superficial branch of ulnar nerve ☐

Musculocutaneous nerve ☐

Ulnar nerve ☐

Superficial branch of radial nerve ☐

Deep branch of radial nerve ☐

Major Nerves of the Lower Limb – anterior view

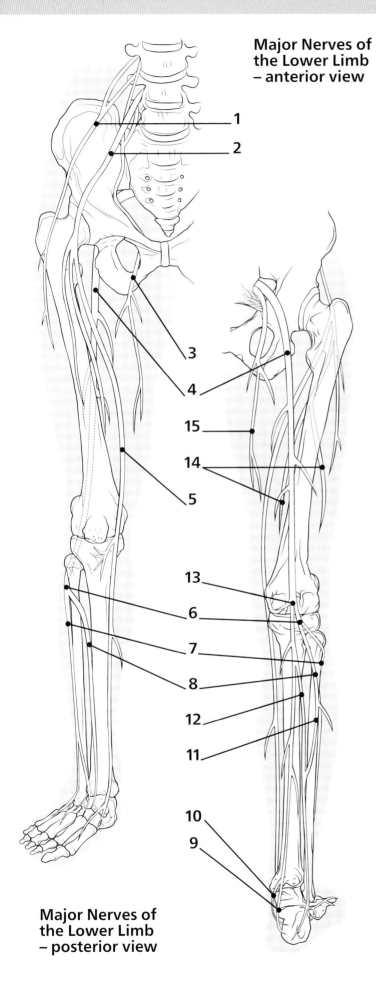

Major Nerves of the Lower Limb – posterior view

i) Add numbers to the boxes below to match each label to the correct part of the artwork

Superficial fibular nerve	☐
Lateral plantar nerve	☐
Saphenous nerve	☐
Sciatic nerve	☐
Obturator nerve	☐
Common fibular nerve	☐
Lateral femoral cutaneous nerve	☐
Deep fibular nerve	☐
Medial plantar nerve	☐
Femoral nerve	☐
Lateral sural cutaneous nerve	☐
Medial sural cutaneous nerve	☐
Posterior femoral cutaneous nerve	☐
Branches from femoral nerve	☐
Tibial nerve	☐

The Brain

The brain, together with the spinal cord, makes up the central nervous system. The brain is responsible for processing sensory information about the world around us and the state of the internal organs of the body. It uses that information to make decisions, whether conscious or unconscious; and produces changes to the environment, either through movement of skeletal or voluntary muscles to influence the external environment, or by actions on glands and smooth muscle to affect the internal environment.

Key terms:

Brainstem A term generally used to mean the midbrain, pons, and medulla oblongata.

Cerebellum The part of the brain below the cerebrum and posterior to the pons of the brainstem. It has a folded cerebellar cortex and is concerned with motor coordination.

Cerebrum The largest part of the brain, including the cerebral hemispheres and the deep structures (e.g. the thalamus) within the forebrain.

Corpus callosum A large fibre bundle joining the two cerebral hemispheres. It carries over 300 million axons to enable cross-talk between the two sides of the forebrain.

Fornix An arching fibre bundle that passes from the hippo-campus and nearby temporal lobe to the septal area and hypothalamus.

Gyrus An elevation of the surface of the cerebral hemisphere. Gyri are separated by sulci.

Hypothalamus The inferior part of the diencephalon. It is concerned with homeostasis (maintaining a constant internal environment), motivation, and control of the autonomic nervous system.

Insula cortex An area of cerebral cortex hidden in the depths of the lateral fissure.

Pineal gland A gland attached to the superior surface of the diencephalon. It secretes the hormone melatonin and is involved in biological rhythms. It is also known as the pineal body.

Sagittal fissure The deep midline groove separating the two cerebral hemispheres. It runs along the line of the sagittal suture of the skull and is occupied by a sheet of dura mater known as the falx cerebri.

Spinal cord The part of the central nervous system that extends from the foramen magnum at the skull base to the intervertebral disc between lumbar vertebrae 1 and 2.

Sulcus A groove on the surface of the cerebral hemisphere. A deep sulcus may be called a fissure.

Thalamus An egg-shaped region on each side of the third ventricle. It acts as a relay station between the brainstem and the cortex. The thalamus contains nuclei concerned with vision, hearing, and touch, as well as nuclei engaged in feedback motor circuits.

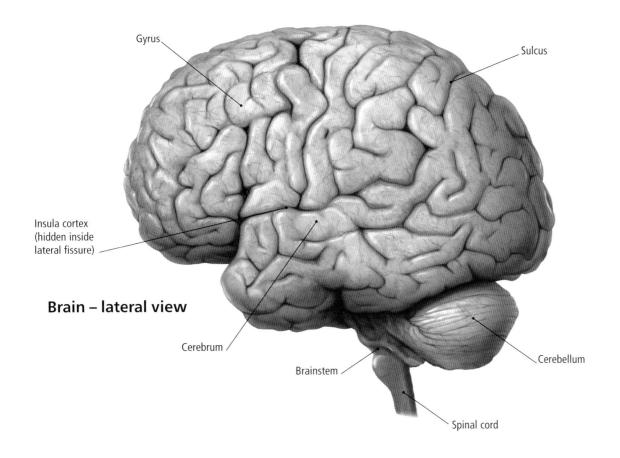

Gyrus

Sulcus

Insula cortex
(hidden inside
lateral fissure)

Brain – lateral view

Cerebrum

Brainstem

Cerebellum

Spinal cord

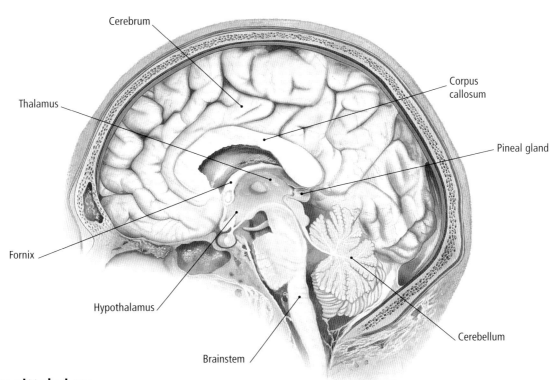

Cerebrum

Corpus
callosum

Thalamus

Pineal gland

Fornix

Hypothalamus

Cerebellum

Brainstem

**Brain – sagittal view
(cut along sagittal fissure)**

The Brain: Lobes and Functional Areas

Each cerebral hemisphere is divided into lobes. Four of these (frontal, parietal, occipital, temporal) are visible on the external surface of the brain, while the fifth (the insula) lies deep within the lateral fissure. The main sensory areas are the primary somatosensory (touch/pain/temperature) area in the parietal lobe, the primary auditory area (temporal lobe), the primary visual area (occipital lobe) and the primary olfactory (smell) area in the medial temporal lobe. The primary motor cortex is in the frontal lobe.

Key terms:

Auditory association area The area of cortex around the primary auditory cortex. It is concerned with higher processing of auditory information (e.g. pitch, timbre, and sound localisation).

Frontal lobe The lobe of the brain deep to the frontal bone. It contains the prefrontal cortex, areas for control of eye movements (frontal eye fields), two types of motor cortex (pre- and primary motor), and Broca's area.

Gyrus An elevation of the surface of the cerebral hemisphere. Gyri are separated by sulci.

Lateral fissure The fissure between the frontal and parietal lobes (superiorly) and the temporal lobe (inferiorly). It conceals the insula.

Motor speech area (Broca's) One of the two traditionally recognised cortical language areas, said to be involved in expressive aspects of speech, but other areas in the insula may also be important. It is located in the inferior frontal gyrus.

Occipital lobe The most posterior lobe of the brain. It contains primary and association visual cortex.

Parietal lobe The lobe of the brain broadly deep to the parietal bone. It contains association cortex for higher processing of somatosensory, auditory, and visual information.

Postcentral gyrus The gyrus that contains the primary somatosensory cortex. It is organised somatotopically (i.e. different parts of the body are represented in different regions of the cortex).

Precentral gyrus (motor cortex) The gyrus that contains the primary motor cortex. It is organised musculotopically (i.e. different parts (muscles) of the body are controlled by different regions).

Prefrontal cortex The part of the frontal cortex concerned with forethought, planning, and social interactions.

Primary auditory cortex The part of the cortex concerned with processing auditory information sent up from the medial geniculate nucleus, the auditory relay nucleus of the thalamus. It projects to the auditory association cortex.

Primary motor cortex The part of the cortex that directly drives motor neurons in the brainstem and spinal cord through long axon pathways. The pathway to the brainstem is called the corticobulbar tract; that to the spinal cord is called the corticospinal tract.

Primary somatosensory cortex The area of cortex that receives input from the ventral posterior nucleus, the somatosensory thalamic relay nucleus. It projects in turn to the somatosensory association cortex.

Primary visual cortex The area of cortex that receives input from the lateral geniculate nucleus, the visual thalamic relay nucleus. It is organised visuotopically (i.e. different parts of the visual world are represented in different regions of the cortex). It projects to the visual association cortex for further visual processing.

Reading comprehension area Also called the visuolexic area. It is concerned with comprehension of written language.

Sensory speech area (Wernicke's) One of the two traditionally recognised cortical language areas. It is said to be concerned with comprehension of spoken language, and is usually located on the posterior superior temporal gyrus (planum temporale) but may also be found in the inferior parietal lobe.

Somatosensory association area Cortex concerned with higher processing of somatosensory information. It generates a three-dimensional model of the world around the individual and of shapes held in the hand.

Sulcus A groove on the surface of the cerebral hemisphere. A deep sulcus may be called a fissure.

Temporal lobe The lobe of the brain adjacent to the temporal bone. It contains the primary auditory and association auditory cortical areas, the hippocampus and the amygdala.

Visual association area The part of the cerebral cortex concerned with higher processing of visual information (colour, visual texture, shape, and form).

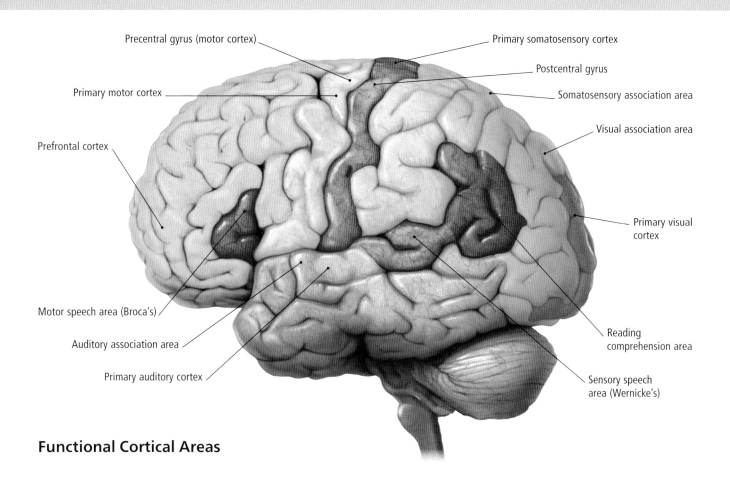

Precentral gyrus (motor cortex)

Primary somatosensory cortex

Primary motor cortex

Postcentral gyrus

Somatosensory association area

Prefrontal cortex

Visual association area

Primary visual cortex

Motor speech area (Broca's)

Reading comprehension area

Auditory association area

Primary auditory cortex

Sensory speech area (Wernicke's)

Functional Cortical Areas

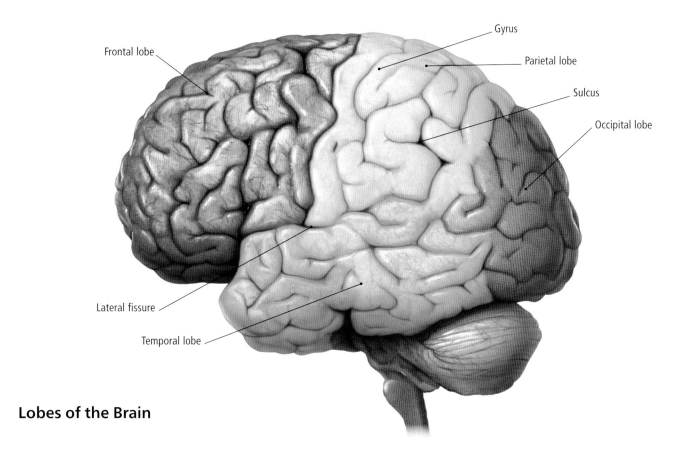

Frontal lobe

Gyrus

Parietal lobe

Sulcus

Occipital lobe

Lateral fissure

Temporal lobe

Lobes of the Brain

True or false?

1   The cell type in the brain that controls the ionic balance of the space between nerve cells is the astrocyte.

2   The main role of the dendrite is to transmit information to other nerve cells.

3   The myelin sheath of an axon can increase the speed of impulse conduction by as much as 100 times.

4   The major cell type in the cerebral cortex is the bipolar cell.

5   The primary motor cortex is located on the postcentral gyrus.

6   The auditory cortex is located on the upper surface of the temporal lobe.

7   The amygdala lies within the temporal lobe of the brain.

8   The corpus callosum is important for transfer of information between functional areas of the two hemispheres.

9   The thalamus is an important way station in the transfer of information from the spinal cord to the cerebral cortex.

10   The highest concentration of nerve cells in the brain is in the granule cell layer of the cerebellum.

11   The cerebral cortex controls the spinal cord motorneurons by the dorsal column pathways.

12   The caudate and putamen play key roles in reward systems and addiction.

13   Parkinson's disease is usually due to degeneration of nerve cells in the substantia nigra.

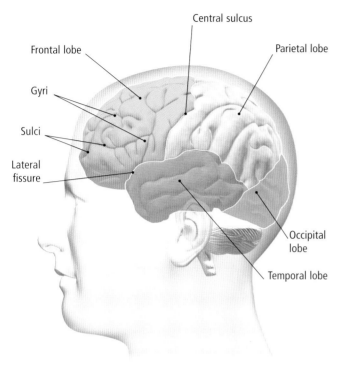

Central sulcus

Frontal lobe

Parietal lobe

Gyri

Sulci

Lateral fissure

Occipital lobe

Temporal lobe

The Cerebral Cortex

The cerebral cortex is divided into four sections called lobes. The frontal and parietal lobes are separated by the central sulcus.

14 *The sense of smell is processed in the parietal lobe of the cerebral cortex.*

15 *Language areas are most often located in the right cerebral hemisphere.*

16 *The hypothalamus is connected to the pituitary by a stalk.*

17 *Reflex centres for the head and neck are located in the brainstem.*

18 *The optic nerve carries motor signals for pupillary dilation.*

19 *Damage to the underside of the temporal lobe on both sides causes an inability to recognise faces.*

20 *Damage to the prefrontal cerebral cortex can cause a change in personality.*

Glioma

Mature neurons do not form tumours, but primary brain tumours (gliomas) may arise within the brain from cells that retain the ability to divide, for example, astrocytes and oligodendrocytes and their precursor cells. The most aggressive primary brain tumour is the glioblastoma multiforme, which probably comes from primitive astrocytes. Gliomas cause headaches, vomiting, seizures, focal neurological signs such as paralysis, sensory loss or specific behavioural change, and cranial nerve dysfunction.

Multiple choice

1 *Which cell type in the brain makes myelin?*
(A) oligodendrocyte
(B) neuron
(C) astrocyte
(D) microglia
(E) choroid plexus

2 *Which cell type in the brain is responsible for immune surveillance?*
(A) Purkinje cell
(B) ganglion cell
(C) endothelium
(D) microglia
(E) choroid plexus

3 *Respiratory centres in the brain are primarily located in the:*
(A) cerebral cortex
(B) thalamus
(C) pons
(D) medulla oblongata
(E) both C and D are correct

4 *Which cranial nerve serves the sense of touch from the face?*
(A) glossopharyngeal nerve
(B) trigeminal nerve
(C) facial nerve
(D) vestibulocochlear nerve
(E) trochlear nerve

5 *The role of the facial nerve is to:*
(A) control the muscles of facial expression
(B) control the parotid salivary gland
(C) serve sensation from the pharynx
(D) control sweat glands of the face
(E) regulate the respiratory rhythm

6 *The vestibulocochlear nerve carries information concerning:*
(A) auditory function
(B) taste from the anterior two-thirds of the tongue
(C) visual function
(D) balance and orientation of the head
(E) both A and D are correct

7 *The hunger and satiety centres are located in the:*
(A) cerebral cortex
(B) thalamus
(C) hypothalamus
(D) cerebellum
(E) pons

8 *The part of the brain responsible for tagging memories with emotional significance is the:*
(A) amygdala
(B) hypothalamus
(C) hippocampus
(D) pons
(E) midbrain

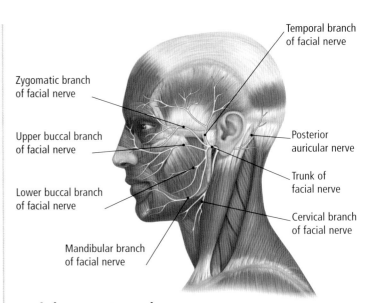

Temporal branch of facial nerve

Zygomatic branch of facial nerve

Upper buccal branch of facial nerve

Lower buccal branch of facial nerve

Mandibular branch of facial nerve

Posterior auricular nerve

Trunk of facial nerve

Cervical branch of facial nerve

Facial Nerve Branches

Note: In this illustration the parotid gland has been removed to reveal the facial nerve branches.

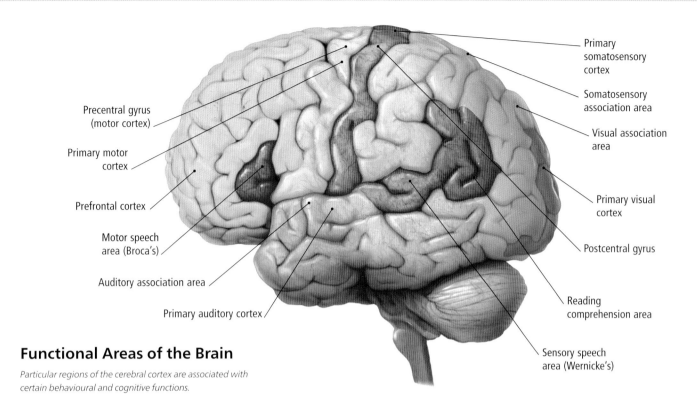

Primary somatosensory cortex

Somatosensory association area

Visual association area

Primary visual cortex

Postcentral gyrus

Reading comprehension area

Sensory speech area (Wernicke's)

Precentral gyrus (motor cortex)

Primary motor cortex

Prefrontal cortex

Motor speech area (Broca's)

Auditory association area

Primary auditory cortex

Functional Areas of the Brain

Particular regions of the cerebral cortex are associated with certain behavioural and cognitive functions.

9   *The ability to lay down new memories is greatly impaired by bilateral damage to the:*
(A)   hippocampus
(B)   amygdala
(C)   hypothalamus
(D)   thalamus
(E)   parietal lobe

10   *The cerebellum receives sensory input from:*
(A)   joint receptors
(B)   inner ear balance organs
(C)   touch receptors on the face
(D)   muscle stretch receptors of the limbs
(E)   all of the above are correct

11   *The primary somatosensory cortex is located on the:*
(A)   precentral gyrus
(B)   postcentral gyrus
(C)   occipital lobe
(D)   orbital cortex
(E)   temporal lobe

12   *Damage to the right parietal lobe can cause:*
(A)   a problem with expressive aspects of speech
(B)   loss of vision in the left visual field
(C)   sensory neglect on the left side of the body
(D)   a problem with working memory
(E)   loss of the sense of smell

13   *Visual information from the left visual field is transmitted to the:*
(A)   left superior colliculus
(B)   right parietal lobe
(C)   right precentral gyrus
(D)   right occipital lobe
(E)   left pons

14   *Working memory (the ability to hold the steps in a simple task in one's memory for a few minutes) is mainly served by the:*
(A)   prefrontal cortex
(B)   parietal lobe
(C)   cerebellum
(D)   hypothalamus
(E)   temporal lobe

Colour and label

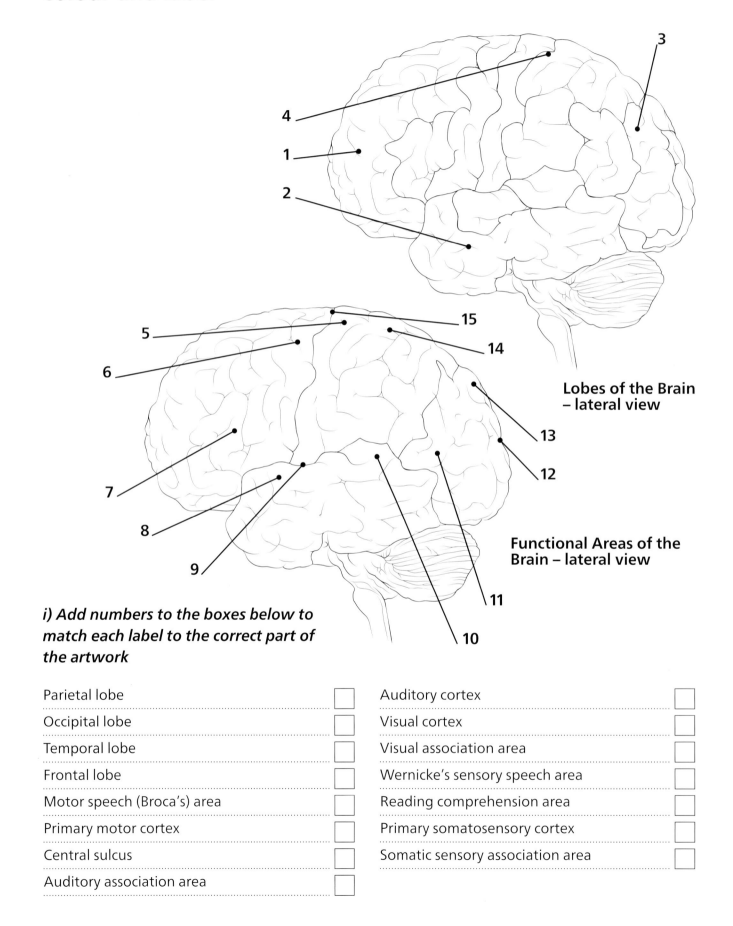

Lobes of the Brain – lateral view

Functional Areas of the Brain – lateral view

i) Add numbers to the boxes below to match each label to the correct part of the artwork

Parietal lobe	☐
Occipital lobe	☐
Temporal lobe	☐
Frontal lobe	☐
Motor speech (Broca's) area	☐
Primary motor cortex	☐
Central sulcus	☐
Auditory association area	☐

Auditory cortex	☐
Visual cortex	☐
Visual association area	☐
Wernicke's sensory speech area	☐
Reading comprehension area	☐
Primary somatosensory cortex	☐
Somatic sensory association area	☐

i) *Label each structure shown on the illustration*

1 ....

2 ....

3 ....

4 ....

5 ....

6 ....

7 ....

8 ....

9 ....

10 ....

11 ....

12 ....

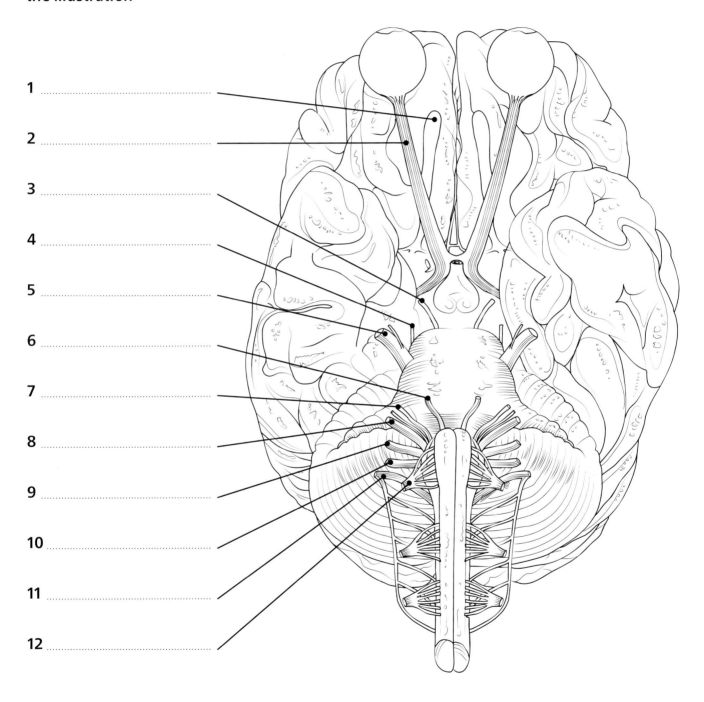

Fill in the blanks

1   The cerebrospinal fluid is mainly made by the _____.

2   The _____ ventricles lie within the cerebral hemispheres.

3   The _____ fluid surrounds the brain and spinal cord.

4   The _____ are veins within the cranial cavity that have been reinforced with dura mater.

5   The _____ is a fibre bundle joining the hippocampus with the hypothalamus.

6   The _____ allows transfer of information between the two cerebral hemispheres.

7   The _____ contains axons connecting the thalamus and cerebral cortex.

8   The _____ is the region where optic nerve axons cross the midline.

9   The _____ nerve supplies the muscles of the tongue.

10   The _____, _____, and _____ nerves supply the skeletal muscles that move the eye.

11   The _____ nucleus is the part of the thalamus that is most concerned with vision.

12   The _____ nucleus is the part of the thalamus that is most concerned with hearing.

13   The _____ peduncle contains axons from the pontine nuclei to the cerebellum.

14   The _____ and _____ nerves are involved in the corneal (blink) reflex.

15   The _____ and _____ nerves are involved in the gag reflex.

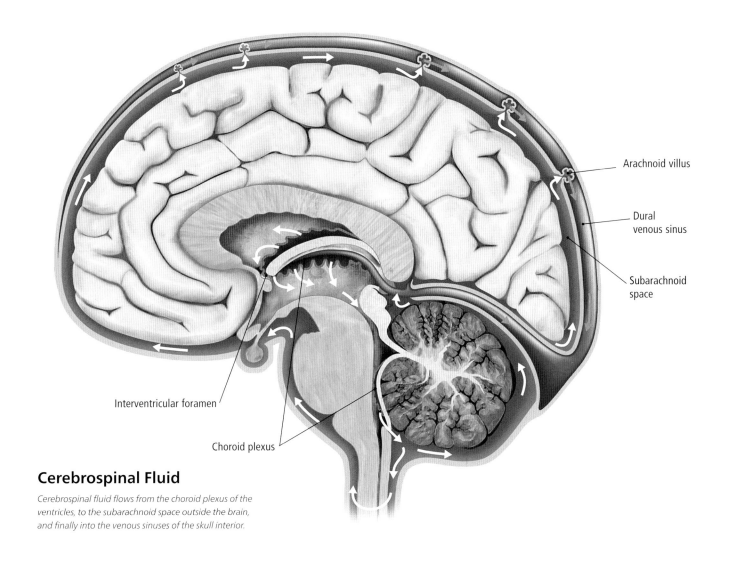

Cerebrospinal Fluid

Cerebrospinal fluid flows from the choroid plexus of the ventricles, to the subarachnoid space outside the brain, and finally into the venous sinuses of the skull interior.

16 The _____ sulcus separates the primary motor and somatosensory cortex.

17 The primary visual cortex is located around the _____ sulcus.

18 The _____ fissure separates the frontal and temporal lobes.

19 The _____ ventricle lies between the pons and the cerebellum.

Match the statement to the reason

1   *Information from ganglion cells in the nasal half of the left retina reaches the left visual cortex because …*

a   *fibres cross in the sensory decussation at the level of the medulla oblongata.*

2   *Information about touch in the right upper limb is represented on the left postcentral gyrus because …*

b   *many descending and ascending axons pass through a narrow space.*

3   *A haemorrhage in the internal capsule can have profound effects on neurological function because …*

c   *the satiety centre is located here.*

4   *A grand mal epileptic seizure appears to spread gradually across the body because …*

d   *axons cross in the chiasm below the hypothalamus.*

5   *A tumour in the hypothalamus can cause obesity because …*

e   *the primary motor cortex has an ordered map of the body parts on it.*

Epilepsy

Epilepsy is a neurological disturbance characterised by abnormal electrical discharges in brain circuitry. Epilepsy may manifest as sensory disturbances, loss of consciousness and convulsions. Epilepsy has many variants ranging from the mild absence attacks of petit mal where the subject transiently loses attention, to tonic/clonic seizures seen in grand mal, where convulsions spread across the body (Jacksonian march) as the abnormal electrical discharge moves across the brain surface. Temporal lobe epilepsy can cause feelings of déjà vu, jamais vu (familiar things seeming new – the opposite of déjà vu), amnesia, olfactory hallucinations and a sudden sense of fear and anxiety.

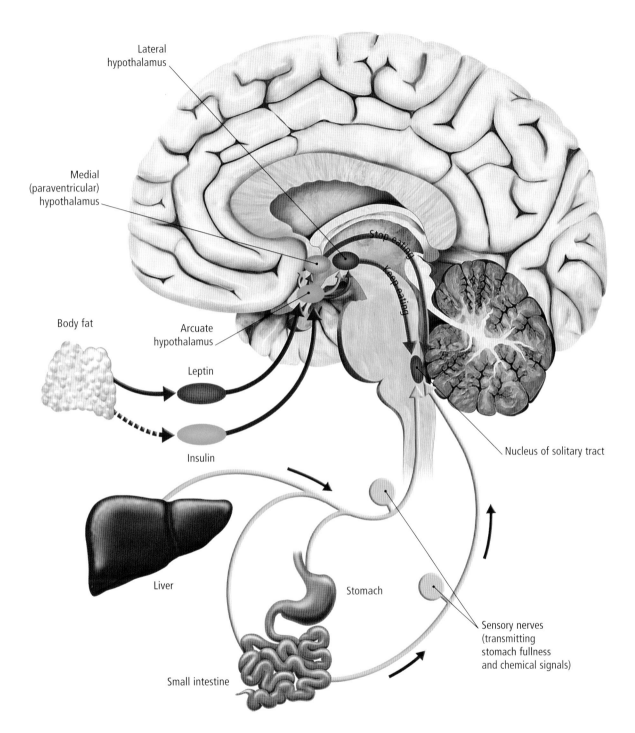

Lateral hypothalamus

Medial (paraventricular) hypothalamus

Stop eating

Keep eating

Body fat

Arcuate hypothalamus

Leptin

Insulin

Nucleus of solitary tract

Liver

Stomach

Sensory nerves (transmitting stomach fullness and chemical signals)

Small intestine

Hypothalamus and Appetite Regulation

Many factors influence the regulation of appetite, and the hypothalamus plays a key role. The amount of body fat influences the hypothalamus through leptin and insulin, hormones that tell the brainstem to stop or continue eating. This interacts with other signals from the liver and gut, via the nucleus of the solitary tract, to influence how hungry we feel.

Colour and label

i) Label each structure shown on the illustration

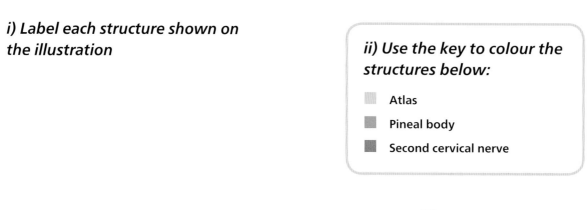

ii) Use the key to colour the structures below:

- Atlas
- Pineal body
- Second cervical nerve

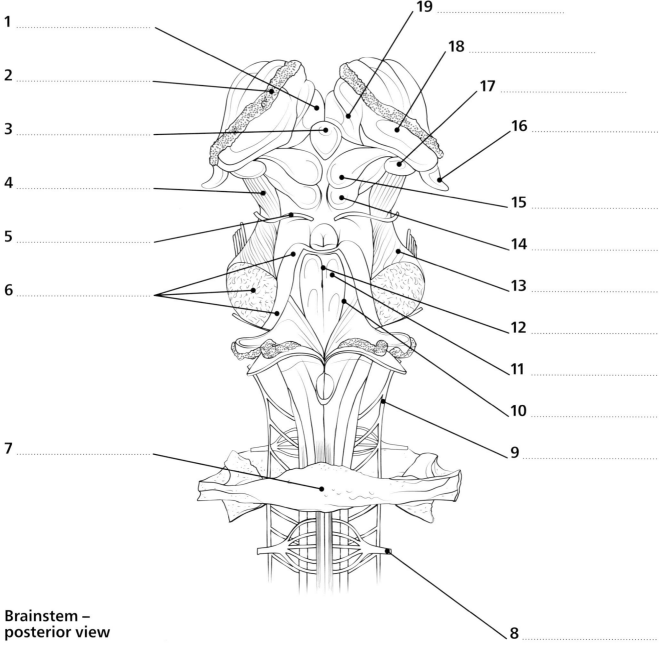

1 ....

2 ....

3 ....

4 ....

5 ....

6 ....

7 ....

19 ....

18 ....

17 ....

16 ....

15 ....

14 ....

13 ....

12 ....

11 ....

10 ....

9 ....

8 ....

**Brainstem –
posterior view**

i) Label each structure shown on the illustrations

Spinal anaesthesia

Anaesthesia of structures in the pelvis or lower limb can be achieved by inserting a depot of local anaesthetic into either the subarachnoid space around the spinal cord (subarachnoid or intrathecal block) or the fat surrounding the spinal nerves (epidural block). Spinal anaesthesia can be used for surgery on the lower limbs, caesarian section and even pelvic surgery. Risks and complications include headache, nerve injury and infection.

Spinal Nerves

1 ....

2 ....

3 ....

4 ....

5 ....

Spinal Cord – anterior view

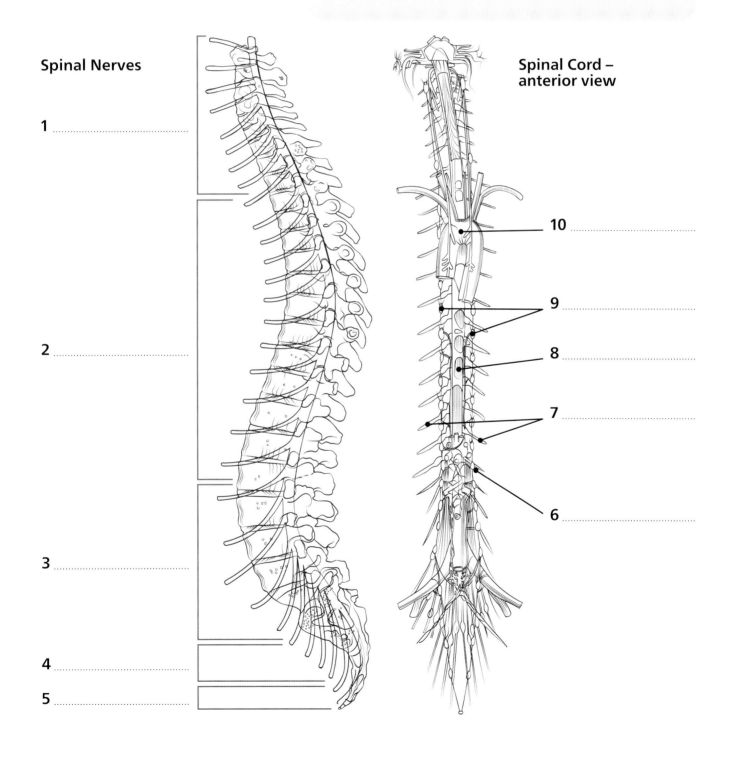

10 ....

9 ....

8 ....

7 ....

6 ....

Special Senses: Sight and Hearing

Key terms:

Anterior chamber The fluid chamber between the posterior surface of the cornea and the iris. It is filled with a watery liquid, the aqueous humour.

Choroid The pigmented and vascularised middle coat of the eye. It provides nutrients by diffusion to the outer retinal layers.

Ciliary body The anterior extension of the choroidal layer of the eye. It connects the choroid with the iris and contains the ciliary muscle and ciliary processes.

Ciliary muscle Smooth muscle that adjusts the tension of the suspensory ligaments on the equator of the lens.

Cornea The thin, convex, transparent surface of the eye. It has no blood vessels and is nourished by diffusion from the surrounding tissues. It is responsible for most of the refraction that produces the image on the retina.

Lens A transparent structure of modifiable shape that allows focusing on near or far objects. Its natural shape is close to spherical, but tension along its equator produces a flattened profile.

Optic nerve The nerve that carries retinal ganglion cell axons from the retina to the visual nucleus of the thalamus (lateral geniculate nucleus), and the midbrain (superior colliculus).

Posterior chamber The fluid chamber between the iris in front and the ciliary body, suspensory ligaments, and lens behind. It is filled with a liquid, the aqueous humour.

Retina The neural layer of the eye. It has layers of photo-receptors, bipolar cells, and ganglion cells, and is richly supplied with blood.

Suspensory ligaments Ligaments attaching the ciliary body to the equator of the lens. When these are relaxed, the lens returns to a more globular shape.

Vitreous body The posterior transparent cavity of the globe of the eye. It is filled with a liquid, the vitreous humour.

The Eye – lateral view

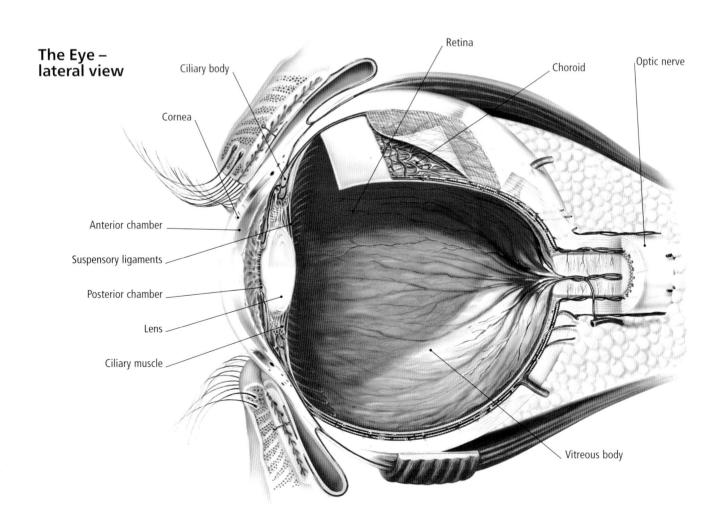

Key terms:

Ampullae Enlarged parts of each semicircular duct. Each one houses a crista, an apparatus for detecting head rotation.

Cochlea Spiral tube of the auditory part of the inner ear.

Cochlear duct The spiral tube that houses the organ of Corti. It is flanked by vestibular and tympanic ducts.

Cochlear nerve The aggregated nerve fibres from the organ of Corti that carry auditory information to the brainstem.

Cochlear (round) window A window between the inner and middle ear. It is covered by the epithelium of the middle ear cavity and bulges outward when the oval window is depressed by the stapes footplate.

Eustachian (auditory) tube A tube connecting the middle ear cavity with the nasopharynx. Allows equalisation of pressure between the two.

External ear canal (meatus) The tube leading from the external environment to the tympanic membrane.

Helicotrema The point near the apex of the cochlea where the vestibular and tympanic ducts communicate.

Incus The middle bone of the auditory ossicle chain.

Malleus The auditory ossicle in direct contact with the tympanic membrane.

Ossicles Three tiny bones arranged in a chain across the middle ear cavity.

Promontory covering first coil of cochlea Bony projection of the medial wall of the middle ear formed by the cochlea's base.

Saccular macula The sensory region of the saccule. Its hair cells are stimulated during linear acceleration of the head.

Saccule One of the components of the vestibular apparatus. It detects linear acceleration of the head.

Semicircular canals Three bony channels (lateral, posterior, and anterior) that house the semicircular ducts.

Stapes A stirrup-shaped bone of the middle ear.

Stapes footplate covering vestibular (oval) window The base or footplate of the stapes sits on the vestibular window and imparts vibrations from the tympanic membrane to the perilymph (a fluid) of the inner ear.

Tympanic duct The spiral channel (scala tympani) that ascends the cochlea from base to apex.

Tympanic membrane (eardrum) The membrane separating the external from the middle ear.

Utricle One of the components of the vestibular apparatus.

Vestibular duct The spiral channel (scala vestibuli) that ascends the cochlea from the base to the apex.

Vestibular nerve branches Nerve fibres from the components of the vestibular apparatus (maculae of the utricle and saccule and ampullae of the semicircular ducts).

The Ear – lateral view

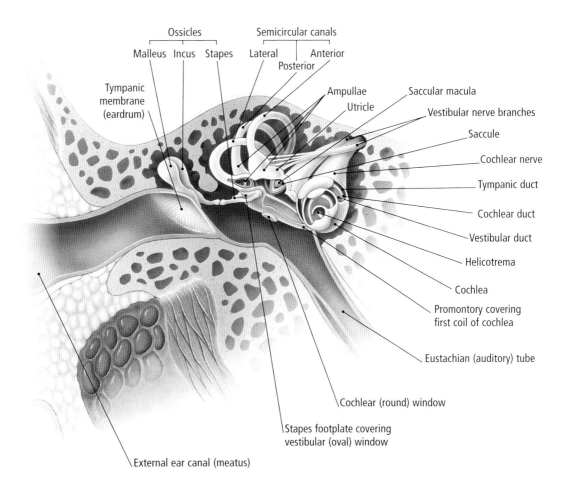

Special Senses: Taste and Smell

Key terms:

Epiglottis A leaf-shaped cartilage that protects the entrance to the larynx. It folds over the laryngeal (airway) entrance during swallowing.

Filiform papillae Conical projections of the dorsum of the tongue. They have no taste buds, but grip food to move it around the mouth.

Foliate papillae Ridges on the posterior edge of the tongue. They have taste buds on their surface.

Fungiform papillae Mushroom-shaped elevations of the tongue surface. Taste buds are found on their surface.

Lingual tonsil (lingual nodules) A lymphoid organ on the surface of the posterior third of the tongue. It is part of an immune surveillance system (Waldeyer's ring) for the entrance to the digestive and respiratory tracts.

Median sulcus The midline groove on the dorsum of the tongue.

Palatine tonsil A lymphoid organ lying at the lateral wall of the oropharynx. It lies between the palatoglossal and palatopharyngeal arches. It is part of an immune surveillance system (Waldeyer's ring) at the entrance to the digestive and respiratory tract.

Palatoglossus muscle and arch The arch at the side of the oral cavity that is produced by mucosa over the palatoglossus muscle. The palatoglossus muscle runs from the soft palate to the tongue.

Palatopharyngeus muscle and arch The arch at the side of the oropharynx that is produced by mucosa over the palatopharyngeus muscle. The palatopharyngeus muscle runs from the soft palate to the muscular wall of the pharynx.

Terminal sulcus A V-shaped depression that separates the anterior two-thirds of the tongue from the posterior third.

Vallate papillae Papillae occupying a depression in the tongue surface. They form a V-shaped line anterior to the terminal sulcus of the tongue. Each vallate papilla has an encircling trench where taste receptors (buds) are located.

Vallecula The depression between the posterior third of the tongue and the epiglottis. It is a potential site for chicken or fish bones to become caught.

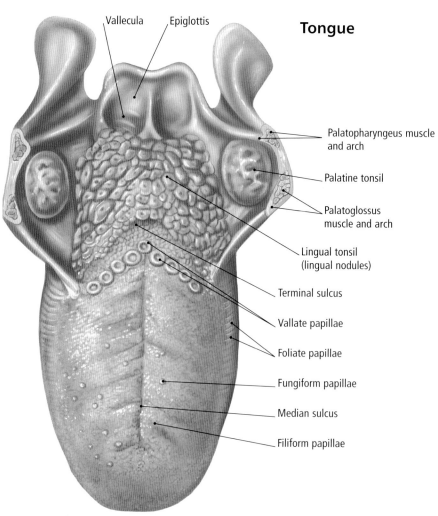

Tongue

Vallecula Epiglottis

Palatopharyngeus muscle and arch

Palatine tonsil

Palatoglossus muscle and arch

Lingual tonsil (lingual nodules)

Terminal sulcus

Vallate papillae

Foliate papillae

Fungiform papillae

Median sulcus

Filiform papillae

Key terms:

Axon The long process of a nerve cell that transmits the impulse to another part of the brain or body.

Bowman's gland (olfactory gland) Gland that produces a serous fluid in which odorant molecules dissolve so they can be presented to the cilia. The secretions also contain an odorant-binding protein that aids the process.

Cilia Hair-like processes from the apices of sensory cells in the nasal mucosa. Odorant molecules lock into receptors on the surface of the cilia.

Cribriform plate of ethmoid bone A delicate plate of bone that forms the roof of the nasal cavity. It is perforated by olfactory nerve fibres.

Fila olfactoria Olfactory nerve fibres passing through the cribriform plate of the ethmoid bone to enter the olfactory bulb.

Frontal lobe The lobe of the brain deep to the frontal bone. It contains the prefrontal cortex, areas for control of eye movements, two types of motor cortex, and Broca's area.

Mitral cell The major output neuron of the olfactory bulb. They project information about smell to the olfactory cortex and olfactory tubercle in the brain.

Olfactory bulb The elongated melon-shaped structure above the cribriform plate of the ethmoid bone. It receives fila olfactoria and processes olfactory information before sending it through the olfactory tract to the olfactory cortex in the brain.

Olfactory mucosa The epithelium of the upper nasal cavity that is sensitive to odorants. It contains four types of cells: mature nerve cells, basal proliferative cells, immature nerve cells, and supporting cells.

Olfactory nerve cell Sensory neuron in the olfactory epithelium. Each cell has an apical process with a knob-like ending and 10–20 cilia that sample the inhaled air for odorant molecules. The other end of the cell has an axon that runs to the olfactory bulb.

Olfactory tract The fibre pathway running from the olfactory bulb to the olfactory centres (olfactory cortex and olfactory tubercle) in the brain.

Olfactory Apparatus

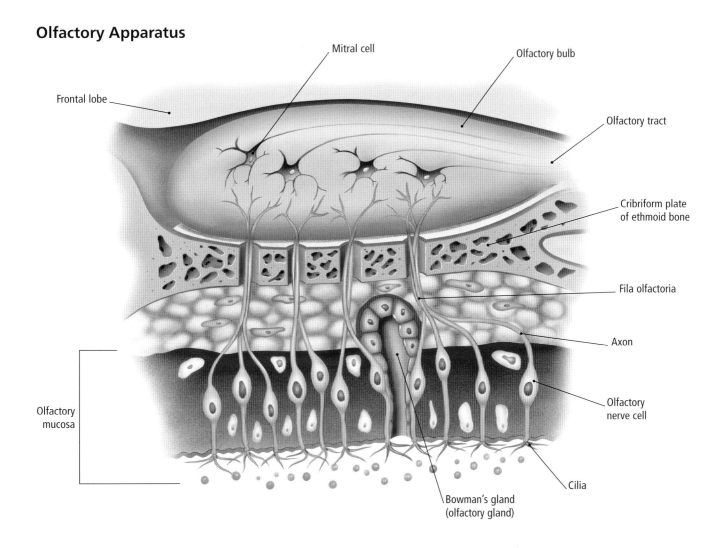

True or false?

**Retina –
cross-sectional view**

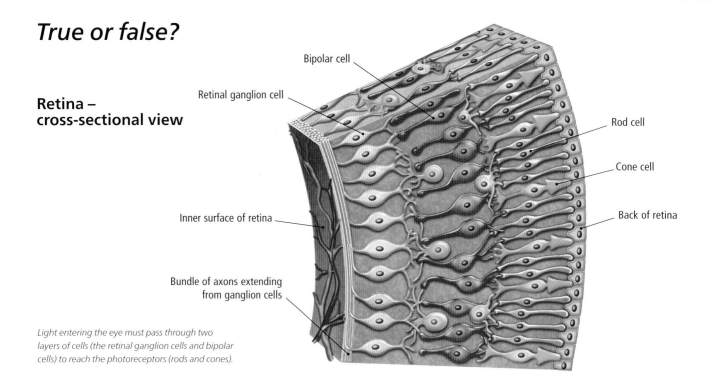

Bipolar cell

Retinal ganglion cell

Rod cell

Cone cell

Inner surface of retina

Back of retina

Bundle of axons extending
from ganglion cells

*Light entering the eye must pass through two
layers of cells (the retinal ganglion cells and bipolar
cells) to reach the photoreceptors (rods and cones).*

1   *Olfactory receptor cells send axons through the cribriform plate of the skull.*

2   *The olfactory region of the cerebral cortex is on the medial temporal lobe.*

3   *The olfactory tract carries parasympathetic axons to the olfactory mucosa.*

4   *Olfactory sensory input has a strong influence on emotional memory.*

5   *Circumvallate papillae have taste buds on their exposed surface.*

6   *Sweet, sour, salt, bitter and umami are the five taste sensations.*

7   *Olfaction plays no role in the tasting of food and drink.*

8   *The lacrimal gland is located in the upper medial part of the orbit.*

9   *The bulbar conjunctiva covers the sclera of the eyeball.*

10 *The ciliary muscle is controlled by the parasympathetic nervous system.*

Cataract

Cataract is a common condition where the lens becomes progressively cloudy or opacified, leading to loss of vision. Patients complain of faded colours, blurring of vision, haloes around lights and difficulty seeing at night. It causes half of the blindness in the world and is most commonly due to ageing, although it can be present at birth. Risk factors for early onset include diabetes mellitus and cigarette smoking. The condition can be treated by removal of the old opacified lens core and replacement with a foldable prosthetic lens.

11   The shape of the lens is controlled by contraction of the ciliary muscle.

12   The vitreous humour fills the anterior chamber of the eye.

13   Rod photoreceptors are most useful for vision in low light levels.

14   Cone photoreceptors are concentrated into a fovea located medial to the optic disc.

15   Retinal ganglion cells send their axons into the optic nerve.

16   The middle ear cavity is filled with perilymph.

17   The pharyngotympanic (auditory) tube connects the middle ear with the oropharynx.

18   The footplate of the stapes lies over the oval window.

19   The macula of the utricle primarily detects linear acceleration of the head.

20   Contraction of the stapedius muscle helps to open the pharyngotympanic (auditory) tube.

Multiple choice

1 Which part of the nasal cavity contains the olfactory sensory region?

(A) the roof
(B) the medial wall
(C) the lateral wall
(D) the floor
(E) the nasal vestibule

2 Nerve fibres from the olfactory sensory region of the nasal cavity terminate in the:

(A) temporal lobe
(B) occipital lobe
(C) amygdala
(D) olfactory bulb
(E) thalamus

3 Taste information is carried to the brainstem by which nerve/s?

(A) trigeminal
(B) facial
(C) glossopharyngeal
(D) vagus
(E) answers B, C and D are correct

4 The facial nerve serves taste to the:

(A) anterior two-thirds of the tongue
(B) soft palate
(C) posterior one-third of the tongue
(D) epiglottis
(E) floor of the mouth

5 Tear fluid from the conjunctival sac drains to the nasal cavity by the:

(A) frontonasal duct
(B) ethmoid air cells
(C) nasolacrimal duct
(D) sphenoid sinus
(E) nasociliary canal

6 The most powerful refractive element of the eye is the:

(A) aqueous humor
(B) cornea
(C) lens
(D) vitreous humor
(E) choroid

7 The three layers of the eyeball are, from outside to inside:

(A) retina, choroid, sclera
(B) retina, sclera, choroid
(C) choroid, sclera, retina
(D) sclera, choroid, retina
(E) choroid, retina, sclera

8 The size of the pupil is controlled by smooth muscle in the:

(A) ciliary body
(B) choroid
(C) iris
(D) retina
(E) orbital margin

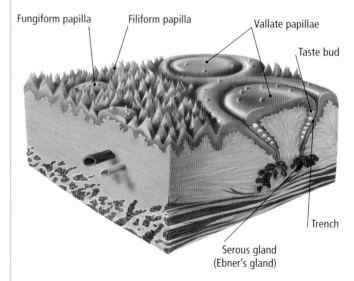

Fungiform papilla   Filiform papilla   Vallate papillae   Taste bud   Trench   Serous gland (Ebner's gland)

Tongue – cross-sectional view

The majority of taste buds are found on the tongue. These taste buds are located in the papillae, which are projections on the upper surface of the tongue.

9 *Which of the following is found in the innermost layer of the retina?*

(A) photoreceptor cell bodies
(B) bipolar cell bodies
(C) amacrine cells
(D) retinal ganglion cell bodies
(E) retinal ganglion cell axons

10 *Which of the following is true concerning the optic disc?*

(A) it is the most light-sensitive part of the retina
(B) it is the site where retinal ganglion cell axons leave the retina
(C) it is the site where the central retinal artery enters the globe of the eye
(D) it is full of rod and cone photoreceptors
(E) both B and C are correct

11 *The boundary between the middle and external ear lies at the:*

(A) oval window
(B) round window
(C) helicotrema
(D) tympanic membrane
(E) external acoustic meatus

12 *The three tiny bones that transmit sound across the middle ear are, from lateral to medial:*

(A) incus, stapes and malleus
(B) malleus, incus and stapes
(C) malleus, stapes and incus
(D) stapes, incus, malleus
(E) stapes, malleus and incus

13 *The main function of the outer hair cells of the organ of Corti is to:*

(A) transduct fluid vibrations in the inner ear to nerve impulses
(B) keep the tectorial membrane clear of debris
(C) move fluid from the scala vestibuli to the cochlear duct
(D) act as a cochlear amplifier to improve auditory sensitivity
(E) produce the fluid of the tunnel of Corti

14 *The sensory organ primarily responsible for detection of rotation of the head in a horizontal plane is the:*

(A) macula of the utricle
(B) macula of the saccule
(C) ampulla of the superior semicircular duct
(D) ampulla of the horizontal semicircular duct
(E) cochlea

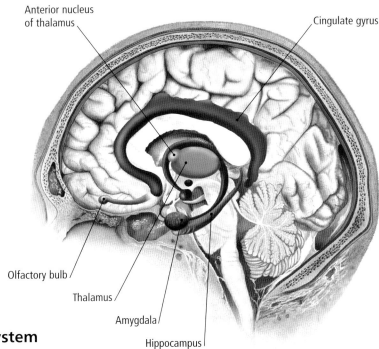

Anterior nucleus of thalamus

Cingulate gyrus

Olfactory bulb

Thalamus

Amygdala

Hippocampus

Smell and the Limbic System

The olfactory bulb is directly connected to the hippocampus and amygdala in the limbic system, which is important for memory and emotion. This is why smells are evocative of past places and feelings, and can trigger responses such as fear and pleasure.

Colour and label

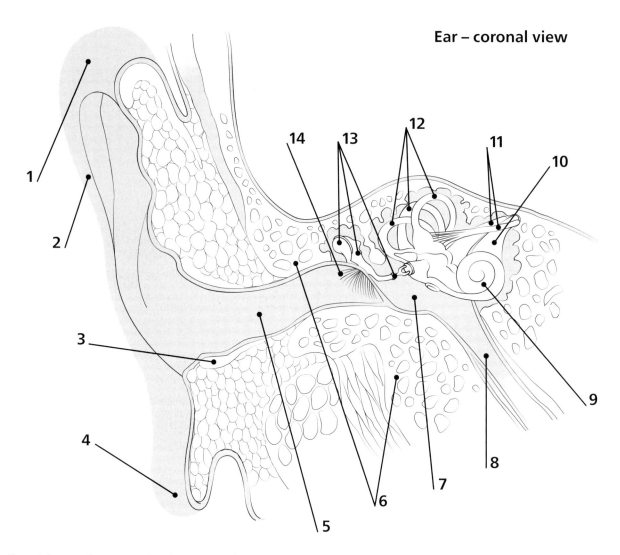

Ear – coronal view

i) Add numbers to the boxes below to match each label to the correct part of the artwork

Lobule	☐	Tympanic membrane (eardrum)	☐
Pinna	☐	Semicircular canals	☐
Cartilage	☐	Cochlear nerve branch	☐
Helix	☐	Vestibular nerve branches	☐
Middle ear (tympanic cavity)	☐	Cochlea	☐
Temporal bone	☐	Ossicles (malleus, incus, and stapes)	☐
External auditory canal (meatus)	☐	Eustachian (auditory) tube	☐

i) Label each structure shown on the illustrations

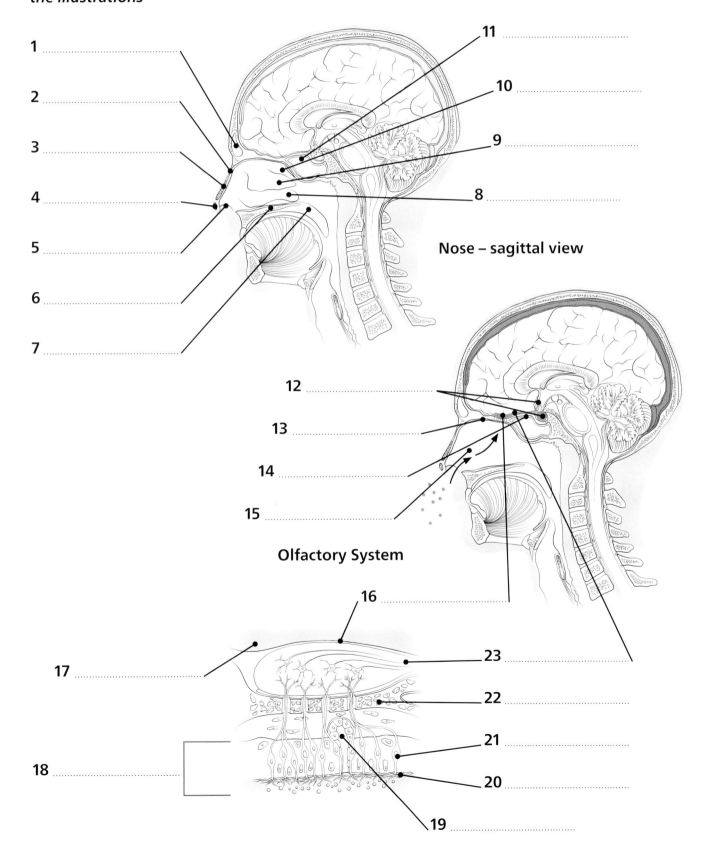

1 ....

2 ....

3 ....

4 ....

5 ....

6 ....

7 ....

11 ....

10 ....

9 ....

8 ....

Nose – sagittal view

12 ....

13 ....

14 ....

15 ....

Olfactory System

16 ....

17 ....

18 ....

23 ....

22 ....

21 ....

20 ....

19 ....

Fill in the blanks

1   The sphincter pupillae and dilator pupillae muscles are under control of the _____
and _____ nervous systems, respectively.

2   The highly coloured part of the eye is the _____.

3   The ciliary muscle is under the control of the _____ nervous system and regulates
the shape of the lens in a process called_____.

4   Much of the oxygen supply to the photoreceptors comes by diffusion from the
_____.

5   The _____ photoreceptors are specialised for monochromatic vision in low
light levels, whereas the _____ photoreceptors serve colour vision under
bright light conditions.

6   Bipolar cells receive input from _____ and pass information to the
_____.

7   Cone photoreceptors are concentrated in a central region of the retina called the
_____, which is specialised for high acuity, colour vision.

8   The utricle and saccule lie within _____ of the _____.

9   The _____ of the organ of Corti are the auditory sensory neurons, whereas the
_____ act as cochlear amplifiers to enhance perception of key frequencies.

10   The fluid within the scala media of the cochlea is called the _____.

11   Blockage of the _____ can cause a middle ear infection known as
_____.

12   The endolymph of the inner ear is manufactured by the _____.

13 The _____ ducts detect rotation of the head by the flow of fluid past the sensory _____ of the ducts.

14 The expanded basal part of the cochlea serves _____ sounds.

15 The _____ division of the _____ nerve arises from utricle, saccule and semicircular duct ampullae of the inner ear.

Ménière's disease

Ménière's disease is a condition affecting the inner ear, where the patient experiences dizziness, tinnitus (ringing in the ear), hearing loss and a feeling of fullness in the ear. The episodes of dizziness tend to last between 20 minutes and an hour. Causes are hereditary and environmental (vascular, viral or autoimmune). The fundamental problem is the build-up of fluid in the inner ear. There is no cure currently, but a low-salt diet, diuretics and anti-inflammatory medication have been tried.

16 The organ of Corti sits on a _____ membrane, the width of which determines the frequency sensitivity of that part of the cochlea.

17 The olfactory receptor neurons have apical processes with _____ and 10 to 20 _____ that sample inhaled air for odorant molecules.

18 Epilepsy in the _____ lobe of the brain can cause olfactory hallucinations.

19 Central regions for taste include the _____ of the brainstem and the _____ of the cerebral cortex.

20 The _____ branch of the _____ nerve conveys taste information from the anterior two-thirds of the tongue.

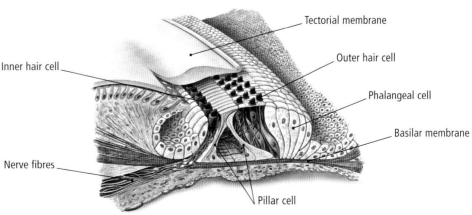

Tectorial membrane
Outer hair cell
Inner hair cell
Phalangeal cell
Basilar membrane
Nerve fibres
Pillar cell

Organ of Corti

The highly sensitive and receptive hair-like cells in the organ of Corti enable us to hear even very faint sounds. The cells are triggered by movement in the cochlear fluid and, when activated, send nerve impulses to the auditory cortex of the brain.

Match the statement to the reason

1   *The human retina receives oxygen and nutrients from two arterial supplies (choroid and central retinal artery branches) because …*

a   *the axons from retinal ganglion cells that 'see' the opposite visual fields pass to the same side of the brain (i.e. the left cortex receives visual information from right visual field halves for each eye).*

2   *Tumours of the pituitary gland can cut off vision in the temporal fields of each eye because …*

b   *the delicate axons of the olfactory receptor neurons pass through tiny holes in the bony cribriform plate and can be severed by a skull base fracture.*

3   *Damage to the primary visual cortex of one side of the brain causes blindness in the paired visual fields towards the opposite side of the body, i.e. blindness in the temporal field for the right eye and nasal field for the left eye from a left visual cortex lesion because …*

c   *the thickness of the human retina is too great for supply of the inner retinal layers from the choroid circulation alone.*

4   *Progressive deafness with age for high auditory tones results from loss of cochlear hair cells from the basal turns of the cochlea because …*

d   *axons from the nasal retina (which 'sees' the temporal visual field due to the image inversion of the eye) cross in the midline directly superior to the anterior lobe of the pituitary.*

5   *Fractures of the skull base from a blow to the nasal bridge can cause loss of the sense of smell (anosmia) because …*

e   *inner hair cells in the basal parts of the cochlea spiral are specifically tuned to perceive sounds of high frequency and are most readily damaged by prolonged exposure to loud noise.*

1 Middle ear infections are more common in children because …

a hair cells in particular parts of the cochlear spiral are tuned to specific frequencies, and an implanted electrode can stimulate the remaining nerve pathways to allow perception of sound.

2 The glands of the external ear produce waxy cerumen because …

b a fluid environment is necessary to present taste molecules (tastants) to the receptors.

3 Cochlear implants can alleviate deafness by threading an electrode around the turns of the cochlear because …

c fatty acids are toxic to many pathogenic microorganisms.

4 Damage to the olfactory mucosa and nerves leads to loss of enjoyment of food because …

d olfaction plays a key role in the 'taste' of food.

5 Food cannot be tasted with a dry mouth because …

e the juvenile auditory tube is more horizontal and drains poorly.

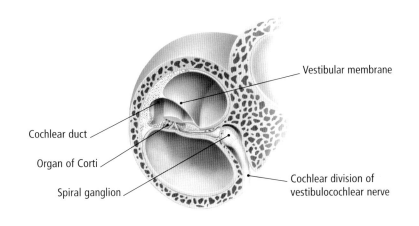

Cochlear duct
Organ of Corti
Spiral ganglion
Vestibular membrane
Cochlear division of vestibulocochlear nerve

Cochlea

The cochlea is a spiral structure of the inner ear, containing three fluid-filled channels. The central channel contains the organ of Corti (see page 117).

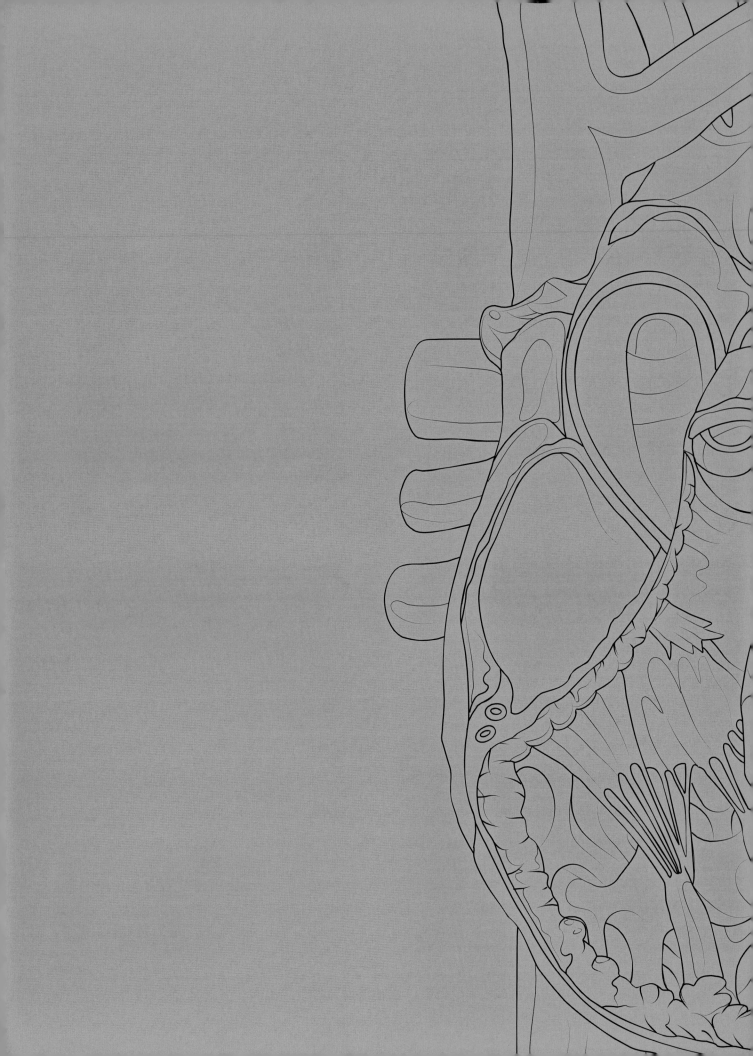

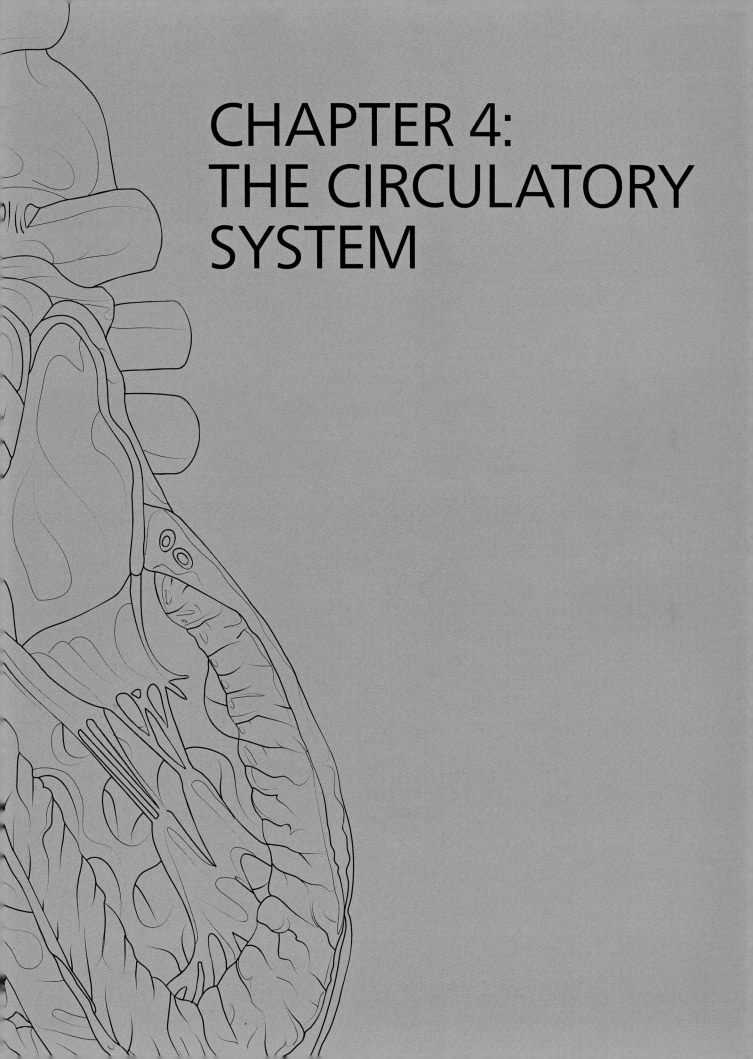

CHAPTER 4:
THE CIRCULATORY SYSTEM

The Heart

The heart is a muscular pump that circulates blood around both the systemic and pulmonary circulations. The systemic circulation carries oxygenated blood from the left side of the heart to the capillaries of all organs except the peripheral lung and returns the deoxygenated blood to the right side of the heart. The pulmonary circulation carries deoxygenated blood from the right side of the heart to the capillaries of the lungs and returns it as oxygenated blood to be pumped through the systemic circulation again.

Key terms:

Aortic arch The most superior part of the aorta. It gives rise to the brachiocephalic artery (trunk), left common carotid artery, and left subclavian artery.

Aortic valve The semilunar valve at the beginning of the aorta. It prevents regurgitation of aortic blood into the left ventricle during ventricular diastole.

Ascending aorta The initial part of the aorta, from the aortic valve to the origin of the brachiocephalic artery (trunk). It gives rise to the coronary arteries.

Brachiocephalic artery (trunk) The brachiocephalic artery is the first branch of the aortic arch. It gives off the right subclavian and right common carotid arteries.

Chordae tendineae Fibrous bands ('heartstrings') which anchor the edges of atrioventricular valve leaflets to the apices of papillary muscles.

Descending aorta The part of the aorta distal to the arch. It supplies the posterior chest wall, spinal cord, abdomen, pelvis, and lower limbs.

Inferior vena cava The largest vein of the abdomen. It carries blood from the lower limb, pelvis, kidneys, and posterior abdominal wall.

Leaflet/cusp of mitral valve One of two leaflets of the mitral valve. The edge of each is anchored by chordae tendineae and a papillary muscle to the left ventricle wall.

Leaflet/cusp of tricuspid valve One of three leaflets of the tricuspid valve. The edge of each is anchored by chordae tendineae and a papillary muscle to the right ventricle wall.

Left atrium The chamber that receives relatively oxygenated blood from the four pulmonary veins and pumps it to the left ventricle.

Left brachiocephalic vein The vein draining systemic venous blood from the left head and neck and left upper limb.

Left common carotid artery The branch of the arch of the aorta that supplies the left head and neck.

Left inferior pulmonary vein One of four veins returning relatively oxygenated blood to the left atrium.

Left pulmonary artery The branch of the pulmonary artery that supplies relatively deoxygenated blood to the left lung.

Left subclavian artery The branch of the arch of the aorta that supplies the left upper limb.

Left superior pulmonary vein One of four veins returning relatively oxygenated blood to the left atrium.

Left ventricle The heart chamber that develops the highest pressure (120 mm Hg) and therefore has the thickest muscle wall. Its interior cavity pumps blood to the ascending aorta.

Opening of coronary sinus The opening of a large vein that drains blood from most of the heart muscle. It enters the right atrium above the opening of the tricuspid valve.

Papillary muscle A small muscular projection that anchors the chordae tendineae and hence atrioventricular valve leaflets to the heart wall. The papillary muscles contract during ventricular systole to keep the valve leaflets closed.

Pericardium A multilayered sac that encloses the heart. The outermost fibrous layer anchors the heart to adjacent structures. The inner, serous double layer provides a fluid-filled space to reduce friction during beating of the heart.

Pulmonary valve The semilunar valve at the ouflow from the right ventricle. It prevents regurgitation of blood from the pulmonary trunk into the right ventricle during diastole.

Right atrium The heart chamber that receives systemic venous blood from the superior and inferior vena cava and the veins draining blood from the heart itself.

Right brachiocephalic vein The vein draining systemic venous blood from the right head and neck and right upper limb.

Right inferior pulmonary vein One of four veins returning relatively oxygenated blood to the left atrium.

Right pulmonary artery The branch of the pulmonary artery that supplies relatively deoxygenated blood to the right lung.

Right superior pulmonary vein One of four veins returning relatively oxygenated blood to the left atrium.

Right ventricle The heart chamber that pumps blood into the pulmonary circulation. It has a thinner wall than the left ventricle because it develops lower pressures (25 mm Hg).

Superior vena cava The large vein that drains blood from the head, neck, and upper limbs into the right atrium of the heart.

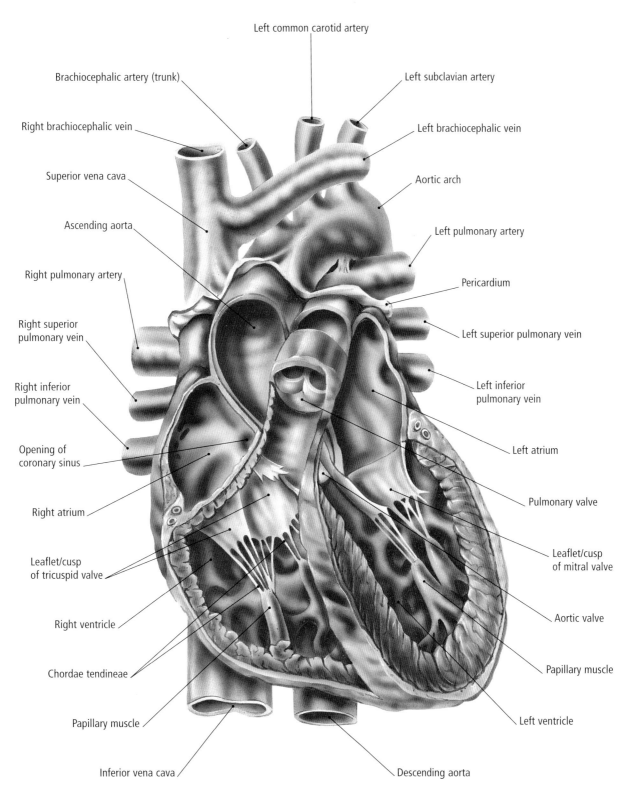

Left common carotid artery

Brachiocephalic artery (trunk)

Left subclavian artery

Right brachiocephalic vein

Left brachiocephalic vein

Superior vena cava

Aortic arch

Ascending aorta

Left pulmonary artery

Right pulmonary artery

Pericardium

Right superior pulmonary vein

Left superior pulmonary vein

Right inferior pulmonary vein

Left inferior pulmonary vein

Opening of coronary sinus

Left atrium

Right atrium

Pulmonary valve

Leaflet/cusp of tricuspid valve

Leaflet/cusp of mitral valve

Right ventricle

Aortic valve

Chordae tendineae

Papillary muscle

Papillary muscle

Left ventricle

Inferior vena cava

Descending aorta

Heart – cross-section

Heart Valves

There are four valves that control the flow of blood through the heart. The two atrioventricular valves (tricuspid or right atrioventricular valve, and mitral or left atrioventricular valve) prevent backflow of blood from the ventricles to the atria at the start of ventricular contraction. The two semilunar valves (pulmonary at the right ventricular outflow, and aortic at the left ventricular outflow) prevent backflow of blood from the pulmonary trunk and ascending aorta into the ventricles at the end of contraction.

Key terms:

Aortic valve See pp. 122–3.

Heart valves Heart valves are found between the atria and ventricles (atrioventricular valves such as the tricuspid and mitral) or at the outflow tracts from the left and right ventricles (aortic and pulmonary semilunar valves, respectively).

Leaflet/cusp of mitral valve See pp. 122–3.

Leaflet/cusp of tricuspid valve See pp. 122–3.

Left atrium See pp. 122–3.

Left ventricle See pp. 122–3.

Mitral valve A two-cusp valve between the left atrium and left ventricle. It is also called the bicuspid valve and is open during ventricular diastole.

Pulmonary valve See pp. 122–3.

Right atrium See pp. 122–3.

Right ventricle See pp. 122–3.

Tricuspid valve A three-cusp valve located between the right atrium and right ventricle. It is also called the right atrioventricular valve.

Ventricular diastole The period of the cardiac cycle when the ventricles are relaxed, and blood flows through the open tricuspid and mitral valves into the ventricles.

Ventricular systole The period of the cardiac cycle when the ventricles contract, expelling blood through the pulmonary and aortic valves.

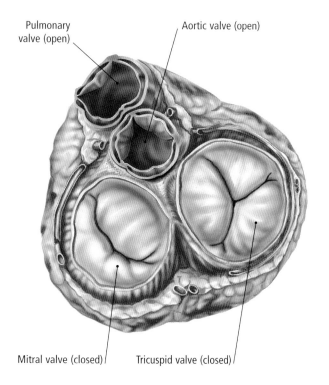

Pulmonary valve (open)

Aortic valve (open)

Mitral valve (closed)   Tricuspid valve (closed)

Ventricular Systole

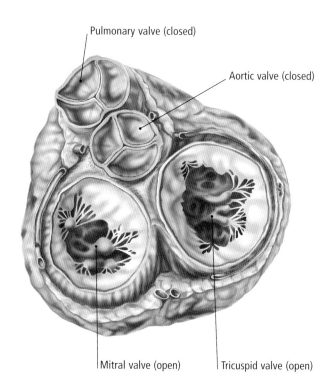

Pulmonary valve (closed)

Aortic valve (closed)

Mitral valve (open)   Tricuspid valve (open)

Ventricular Diastole

Tricuspid Valve

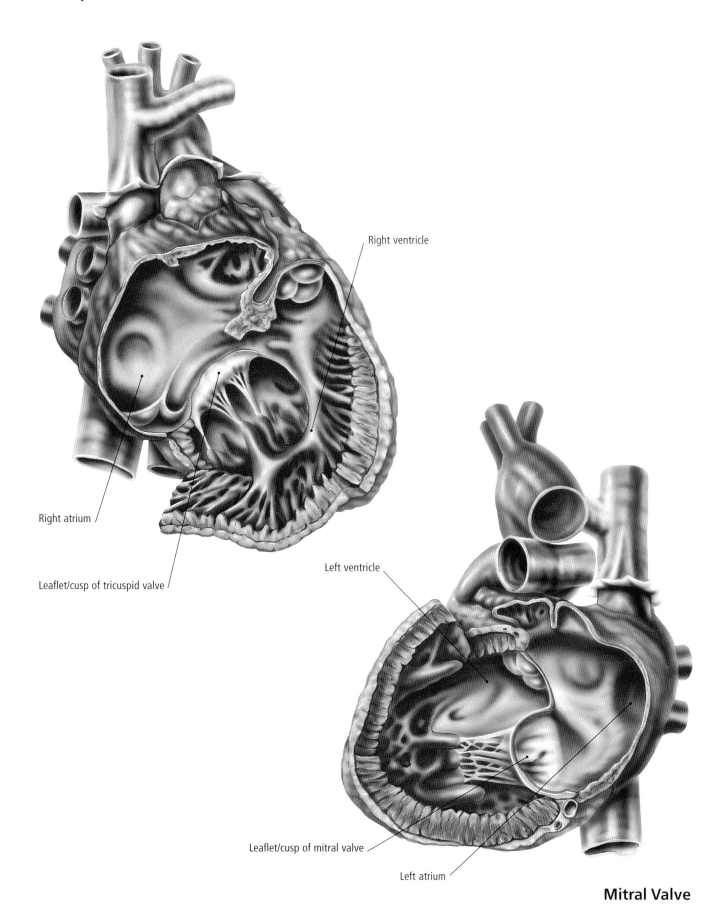

Right ventricle

Right atrium

Leaflet/cusp of tricuspid valve

Left ventricle

Leaflet/cusp of mitral valve

Left atrium

Mitral Valve

True or false?

1   *The heart is mainly found behind the right side of the chest wall.*

2   *The heart is surrounded by an inner fibrous and outer serous pericardium.*

3   *The heart is divided into two atria and two ventricles.*

4   *The right side of the heart receives blood from the pulmonary veins.*

5   *The right atrium receives blood from the superior and inferior vena cava.*

6   *The aorta arises from the left ventricle.*

7   *There is one pulmonary vein on each side.*

8   *The muscle layer of the left ventricular wall is thinner than that of the left atrium.*

9   *The left atrium receives venous blood from the pulmonary circulation.*

10   *The septum between the left and right atria is the thickest wall in the heart.*

11   *The two cardiac semilunar valves are the aortic and pulmonary.*

12   *Highly oxygenated blood flows through the pulmonary artery.*

13   *The mitral valve is between the left and right atria.*

14   *The trabeculae carneae are the muscular ridges and bridges on the interior of the ventricles.*

15   *The heart chambers are lined with pericardium.*

16   *The right atrium has a completely smooth interior.*

17 *Both atria have anterior ear-shaped appendages called the auricles.*

18 *The bridge from the ventricular septum to the base of the anterior papillary muscle carries part of the right bundle branch of the conducting/ pacemaking system.*

19 *The heart chamber at the posterior base of the heart is the right atrium.*

20 *A prominent interventricular sulcus marks the boundary between the two ventricles.*

Myocardial infarction

Myocardial infarction is the death (infarction) of heart muscle (myocardium) due to inadequate blood supply. This is usually due to obstruction, by atherosclerosis, of the coronary arteries supplying the heart muscle. When a partially obstructed artery is completely blocked by a thrombus (blood coagulation), the patient experiences the sudden onset of a crushing pain behind the sternum, which cannot be relieved by anti-angina medication. Complications of infarction include arrhythmias (problems with heart rhythm), which may be the often-fatal ventricular fibrillation, and heart rupture due to weakening of the heart wall.

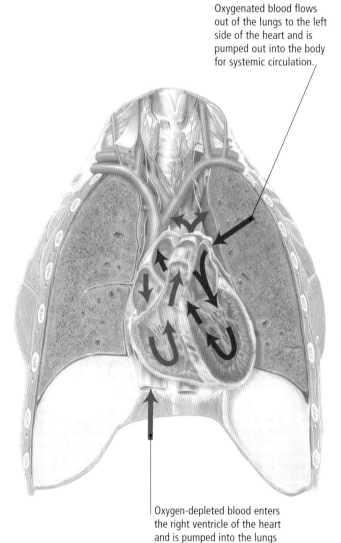

Oxygenated blood flows out of the lungs to the left side of the heart and is pumped out into the body for systemic circulation.

Oxygen-depleted blood enters the right ventricle of the heart and is pumped into the lungs to be oxygenated by the alveoli.

Pulmonary Circulation

The pulmonary system carries deoxygenated blood to the lungs where gas exchange occurs. Carbon dioxide – picked up by the blood from cells and tissues in exchange for oxygen – is exchanged in the lungs for fresh supplies of oxygen. That carbon dioxide is then exhaled, while the now oxygen-rich blood is returned to the heart for another circuit of the body.

Multiple choice

1   *Which of the following structures has the thickest wall?*
- (A)   left atrium
- (B)   right atrium
- (C)   left ventricle
- (D)   right ventricle
- (E)   aorta

2   *At which of the following sites would the oxygen concentration be highest?*
- (A)   left atrium
- (B)   pulmonary artery
- (C)   superior vena cava
- (D)   right atrium
- (E)   right ventricle

3   *Auricular appendages are attached to which heart chambers?*
- (A)   left atrium and left ventricle
- (B)   left and right atria
- (C)   left and right ventricles
- (D)   right ventricle only
- (E)   right atria and right ventricle

Rheumatic heart disease

The lining of the heart's valves shares some antigens (molecules capable of inducing an immune response) with those on the cell wall of group A streptococcal bacteria. When the body's immune system mounts a response to those bacteria following throat infection, damage may also occur to the heart valves. This can cause serious damage, leading to fibrosis and scarring of the valve leaflets. Valve leaflets may stick together, causing valvular stenosis (narrowing), or stick to the vessel wall, causing valvular incompetence. Both of these have long-term adverse effects on heart function.

4   *Which chamber or structure forms the base of the heart?*
- (A)   left ventricle
- (B)   right ventricle
- (C)   left atrium
- (D)   right atrium
- (E)   arch of aorta

5   *Which chamber or structure forms the apex of the heart?*
- (A)   left atrium
- (B)   right atrium
- (C)   arch of aorta
- (D)   right ventricle
- (E)   left ventricle

6   *Which of the following structures attaches directly to the edges of the atrioventricular valve cusps?*
- (A)   musculi pectinati
- (B)   papillary muscles
- (C)   trabeculae carneae
- (D)   chordae tendineae
- (E)   interventricular septum

7   *Which of the following structures prevents regurgitation of blood into the left atrium?*
- (A)   tricuspid valve
- (B)   aortic valve
- (C)   pulmonary valve
- (D)   mitral valve
- (E)   interatrial septum

8   *How thick is the left ventricle wall compared to the right ventricle wall?*
- (A)   the same thickness
- (B)   half as thick as the right ventricle wall
- (C)   one quarter as thick as the right ventricle wall
- (D)   twice as thick as the right ventricle wall
- (E)   almost three times as thick as the right ventricle wall

9 *What is the source of oxygenated blood to the heart muscle?*
Ⓐ coronary sinus
Ⓑ inferior vena cava
Ⓒ coronary arteries
Ⓓ pulmonary trunk
Ⓔ pulmonary veins

10 *Which vessel usually supplies the largest volume of heart muscle?*
Ⓐ pulmonary trunk
Ⓑ right coronary artery
Ⓒ phrenic artery
Ⓓ left coronary artery
Ⓔ coronary sinus

11 *Where is the sinoatrial node located?*
Ⓐ left atrium
Ⓑ right atrium
Ⓒ left ventricle
Ⓓ right ventricle
Ⓔ superior vena cava

12 *Where is the atrioventricular node located?*
Ⓐ right atrium
Ⓑ left atrium
Ⓒ left ventricle
Ⓓ right ventricle
Ⓔ superior vena cava

13 *Which structure drains most venous blood from the heart?*
Ⓐ right coronary vein
Ⓑ superior vena cava
Ⓒ azygos vein
Ⓓ coronary sinus
Ⓔ left coronary vein

14 *The first heart sound is due to the:*
Ⓐ closure of the aortic valve
Ⓑ closure of the pulmonary valve
Ⓒ opening of the aortic valve
Ⓓ opening of the tricuspid and mitral valves
Ⓔ closure of the tricuspid and mitral valves

15 *The second heart sound is due to the:*
Ⓐ closure of the aortic and pulmonary valves
Ⓑ closure of the mitral valve only
Ⓒ opening of the aortic valve
Ⓓ opening of the tricuspid and mitral valves
Ⓔ closure of the tricuspid and mitral valves

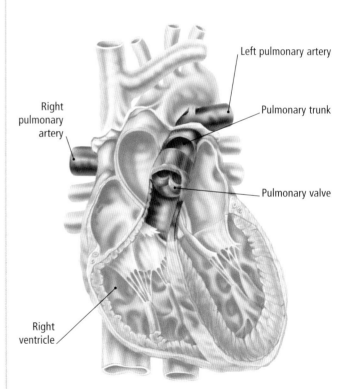

Left pulmonary artery
Right pulmonary artery
Pulmonary trunk
Pulmonary valve
Right ventricle

Pulmonary Artery

Deoxygenated blood is pumped from the right side of the heart to the lungs through the pulmonary artery and its branches.

Colour and label

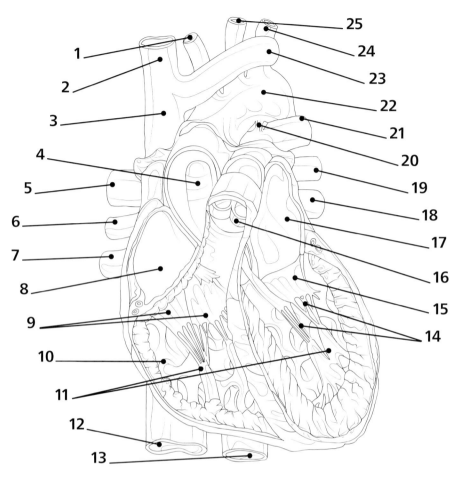

Heart – cross-sectional view

i) Colour the arteries in red, and the veins in blue

ii) Add numbers to the boxes below to match each label to the artwork

Left pulmonary artery	☐
Left superior pulmonary vein	☐
Cusp of mitral valve	☐
Right atrium	☐
Aortic arch	☐
Descending thoracic aorta	☐
Left subclavian artery	☐
Left common carotid artery	☐
Cusp of tricuspid valve	☐
Right ventricle	☐
Papillary muscles	☐
Inferior vena cava	☐

Left atrium	☐
Superior vena cava	☐
Ascending aorta	☐
Right pulmonary artery	☐
Chordae tendineae	☐
Right inferior pulmonary vein	☐
Right superior pulmonary vein	☐
Right brachiocephalic vein	☐
Left brachiocephalic vein	☐
Left inferior pulmonary vein	☐
Ligamentum arteriosum	☐
Brachiocephalic artery	☐
Pulmonary valve	☐

i) Label each structure shown on the illustration

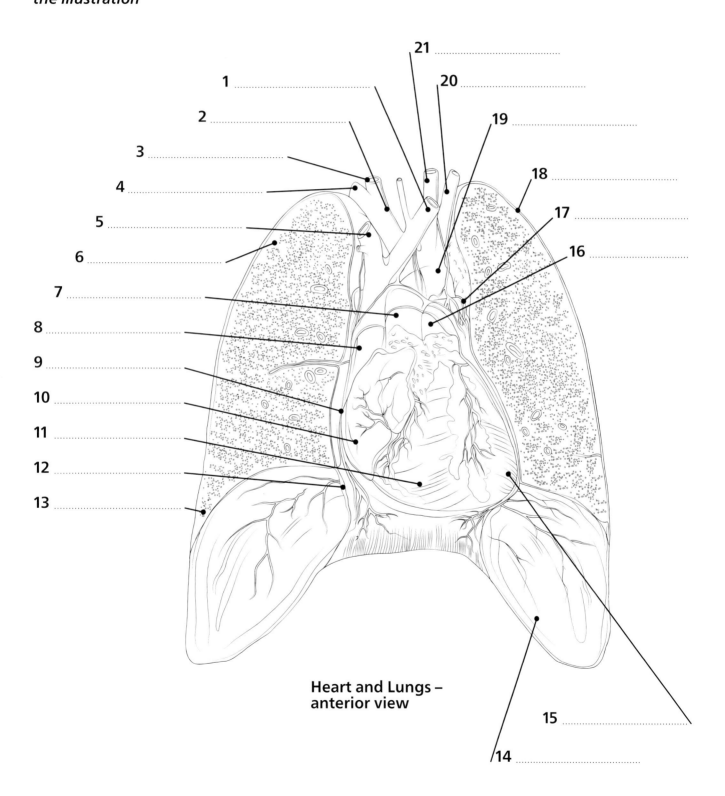

1 ....
2 ....
3 ....
4 ....
5 ....
6 ....
7 ....
8 ....
9 ....
10 ....
11 ....
12 ....
13 ....

14 ....
15 ....
16 ....
17 ....
18 ....
19 ....
20 ....
21 ....

Heart and Lungs – anterior view

Fill in the blanks

1   *Venous blood from the heart muscle mainly drains into the right atrium through the* _____.

2   *The coronary arteries to the heart muscle branch from the* _____.

3   *The* _____ *of the heart points downwards and to the left.*

4   *The interventricular septum has both* _____ *and* _____ *parts.*

5   *The* _____ *valve is between the right atrium and right ventricle.*

6   *The* _____ *carries deoxygenated blood to the lungs.*

7   *Deoxygenated blood enters the heart at the* _____.

8   *The right auricle curls around the* _____.

9   *The muscular ridges on the interior of the ventricles are called* _____.

10   *The muscular ridges on the interior of the atria are called* _____.

11   *The* _____ *is the source of blood for the pulmonary artery.*

12   *The* _____ *forms the left or pulmonary side of the heart.*

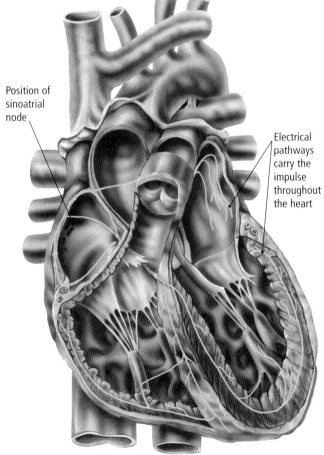

Position of sinoatrial node

Electrical pathways carry the impulse throughout the heart

Heartbeat

The rhythmic beating of the heart is controlled by the sinoatrial node, which transmits electrical impulses to initiate contraction of the heart muscle.

Match the statement to the reason

1 The coronary arteries arise from the aorta because …

a it must develop very high pressure during contraction (over 120 mm Hg) and needs to be very strong.

2 The cardiac veins drain into the right atrium because …

b the atrial muscle must be activated as a single electrical unit before the ventricles are activated, so that atrial contraction precedes ventricular contraction.

3 The muscular wall of the left ventricle is very thick because …

c they must supply oxygenated blood to cardiac muscle, and it is best that this comes from the outflow of oxygenated blood from the left ventricle.

4 A papillary muscle would contract along with the rest of the ventricular muscle because …

d the atrioventricular valve leaflets must be pulled shut to prevent regurgitation of blood into the atria during ventricular contraction.

5 There is an insulating layer of connective tissue between the atrial and ventricular muscles because …

e they carry deoxygenated blood from the cardiac muscle, and this is logically best returned to the chamber of the heart where deoxygenated blood is received.

Arteries

Arteries carry blood away from the heart and are high-pressure vessels. The largest artery in the body is the aorta, which gives off branches to the head, neck and upper limb (brachiocephalic trunk, common carotid, subclavian) before descending to supply the chest wall (by the intercostal arteries), gut organs (by the coeliac and mesenteric arteries), kidneys (by the renal arteries) and pelvic organs, buttock and lower limb (by the internal iliac, external iliac and femoral arteries).

Key terms:

Anterior tibial artery A branch of the popliteal artery that supplies the anterior compartment of the leg.

Aorta The largest artery of the body. It consists of an initial arch arising from the heart, followed by thoracic and abdominal segments.

Aortic arch The most superior part of the aorta. It gives rise to the brachiocephalic artery (trunk), left common carotid artery, and left subclavian artery.

Axillary artery The continuation of the subclavian artery. It gives off branches to the adjacent muscles, a collateral circulation around the glenohumeral joint, and becomes the brachial artery at the lower border of teres minor.

Brachial artery The largest artery of the arm. It is a continuation of the axillary artery and gives off the profunda brachii, radial, and ulnar branches, as well as collateral branches around the elbow joint.

Common carotid artery Supplies the head and neck. Each common carotid divides into an external carotid artery (for the face, scalp, and throat) and an internal carotid artery (for the brain, pituitary gland, and eye).

Common iliac artery The two terminal branches of the abdominal aorta. They divide into external and internal iliac arteries.

Descending aorta The part of the aorta distal to the arch. It supplies the posterior chest wall, spinal cord, abdomen, pelvis, and lower limbs. It divides at the level of lumbar vertebra 4 into two common iliac arteries.

Dorsal arch The dorsal arterial arch of the foot is supplied by the anterior tibial artery and its superficial continuation, the dorsalis pedis artery.

External iliac artery The branch of the common iliac artery that becomes the femoral artery at the inguinal ligament.

Facial artery A branch of the external carotid artery that supplies the face, throat, and anterior neck.

Femoral artery The continuation of the external iliac artery after it passes under the inguinal ligament. Passes through the femoral triangle and gives off the profunda femoris artery before passing through the adductor opening to become the popliteal artery.

Fibular artery A branch of the posterior tibial artery that supplies the posterior compartment of the leg.

Heart A four-chambered muscular pump in the middle mediastinum of the chest.

Intercostal arteries Branches of the aorta or highest intercostal artery that run in the costal groove beneath each rib. They supply the lateral chest wall and anastomose with branches of the internal thoracic artery toward the front of the chest.

Internal iliac artery The branch of the common iliac artery that supplies the gluteal region, pelvic organs, medial pelvic wall, and perineum (space between the thighs).

Obturator artery A branch of the internal iliac (or sometimes the external iliac) artery that supplies the medial pelvic wall and medial upper thigh.

Palmar arterial arches Superficial and deep palmar arches receive blood from the ulnar and radial arteries and give off branches to the palm and digits.

Plantar arch An arterial arch on the plantar side of the distal foot, fed by the posterior tibial artery.

Popliteal artery The continuation of the femoral artery that passes through the popliteal fossa behind the knee. It gives off posterior tibial and fibular arteries.

Posterior auricular artery A branch of the external carotid artery that runs through the parotid gland to divide into auricular and occipital branches near the mastoid process.

Posterior tibial artery A branch of the large artery behind the knee (popliteal artery).

Radial artery One of two arteries of the forearm. It is palpable on the lateral anterior surface of the distal wrist and is used to assess the arterial pulse.

Renal artery The artery supplying the kidney. It also gives branches to the suprarenal (adrenal) gland and the ureter. It arises from the abdominal aorta at the level of the disc between the first and second lumbar vertebrae.

Subclavian artery Arises from brachiocephalic trunk (on right) or the aortic arch (on left). Crosses first rib posterior to the scalene tubercle to become the axillary artery.

Ulnar artery The branch of the brachial artery that supplies the medial forearm.

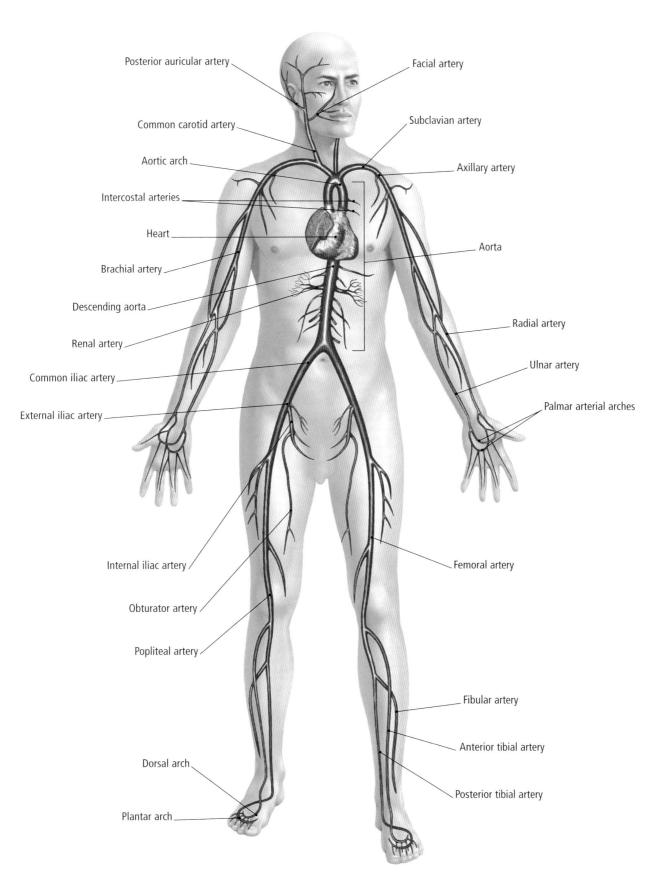

Posterior auricular artery

Facial artery

Common carotid artery

Subclavian artery

Aortic arch

Axillary artery

Intercostal arteries

Heart

Aorta

Brachial artery

Descending aorta

Radial artery

Renal artery

Ulnar artery

Common iliac artery

Palmar arterial arches

External iliac artery

Internal iliac artery

Femoral artery

Obturator artery

Popliteal artery

Fibular artery

Anterior tibial artery

Dorsal arch

Posterior tibial artery

Plantar arch

**Major Arteries of the Body
– anterior view**

Arteries of the Brain

The brain is supplied by four arteries: two internal carotid arteries and two vertebral arteries, although the contribution by the vertebral arteries is probably only 10 per cent. These vessels feed an arterial circle (the circle of Willis), which helps to evenly distribute arterial flow to all cerebral artery branches. The blood from the internal carotid is distributed to the front and middle forebrain, whereas blood from the vertebral system flows to the brainstem, cerebellum and posterior cerebral hemisphere.

Key terms:

Anterior cerebral artery The anterior branch of the internal carotid artery at the circle of Willis. It supplies the orbital cortex, medial frontal lobe, and the corpus callosum.

Anterior communicating artery The small artery joining the anterior cerebral arteries to complete the circle of Willis.

Anterior inferior cerebellar artery A branch of the basilar artery. Supplies the superior pons and anterior cerebellum.

Basilar artery A large midline artery formed from the junction of the vertebral arteries. Supplies the pons and divides to give the posterior cerebral arteries.

Calcarine branch The branch of the posterior cerebral artery that supplies the central part of the primary visual cortex.

Callosomarginal artery A branch of the anterior cerebral artery that ascends into the callosomarginal sulcus.

Circle of Willis The vascular ring at the base of the brain that receives the internal carotid and vertebral arteries, and gives off branches to the forebrain and superior brainstem. It helps to maintain blood supply to the brain when one branch suffers partial or temporary obstruction.

Dorsal branch to corpus callosum One of the terminal branches of the anterior cerebral artery to the corpus callosum.

Internal carotid artery The artery supplying the anterior and lateral parts of the cerebral cortex and much of the deep white matter. It is a branch of the common carotid artery.

Labyrinthine artery A basilar artery branch to the inner ear. It supplies the cochlear and vestibular apparatus.

Medial frontal branches Branches (anterior, intermediate, and posterior) of the anterior cerebral artery to the supplementary motor cortex.

Medial frontobasal artery An arterial branch to the orbital surface of the frontal lobe.

Medial occipital artery (branch of posterior cerebral artery) An artery supplying the medial primary and association visual cortex.

Medial striate artery An arterial branch of the circle of Willis to the deep structures of the medial forebrain.

Middle cerebral artery The largest branch of the internal carotid artery. Runs in the lateral fissure to supply the lateral parts of the frontal, parietal, and temporal cortex, and the insula. Its region of supply includes most of the motor and primary somatosensory cortex, primary auditory cortex, and language areas. It also supplies the deep white and grey matter structures of the forebrain.

Paracentral artery A branch of the anterior cerebral artery to the paracentral lobule (lower limb region of the primary motor and somatosensory cortex).

Parietooccipital branch A branch of the posterior cerebral artery that runs in the parietooccipital fissure to supply the visual association cortex.

Pericallosal artery A branch of the anterior cerebral artery that courses around the corpus callosum.

Polar frontal artery A branch of the anterior cerebral artery to the frontal pole of the cerebrum.

Posterior cerebral artery The terminal branch of the basilar artery. It supplies the posterior occipital lobe, in particular the primary and association visual cortex.

Posterior communicating artery An artery joining the carotid- and basilar-derived parts of the circle of Willis. Runs between the internal carotid and posterior cerebral arteries.

Posterior inferior cerebellar artery A branch of the vertebral artery that supplies the lateral parts of the medulla and the posterior inferior cerebellum.

Precuneal artery A branch of the anterior cerebral artery that supplies the part of the medial cerebral surface between the primary somatosensory cortex and the visual association cortex.

Right anterior cerebral artery An anterior branch of the circle of Willis that supplies the medial anterior forebrain, including the supplementary motor cortex and the medial parts of the primary motor and somatosensory cortex.

Superior cerebellar artery A branch of the basilar artery that supplies the superior parts of the cerebellum.

Vertebral artery A branch of the subclavian artery that ascends the neck through the transverse foramina of the upper six cervical vertebrae. It enters the cranial cavity through the foramen magnum to supply the brainstem and occipital lobe.

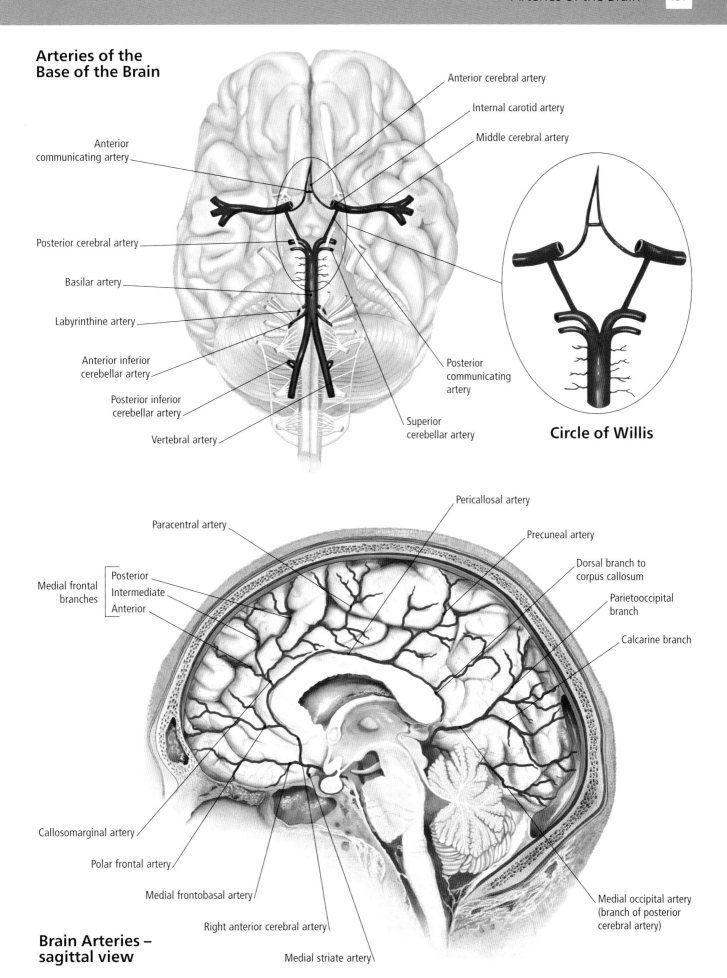

Arteries of the Base of the Brain

Anterior cerebral artery

Internal carotid artery

Middle cerebral artery

Anterior communicating artery

Posterior cerebral artery

Basilar artery

Labyrinthine artery

Anterior inferior cerebellar artery

Posterior inferior cerebellar artery

Vertebral artery

Posterior communicating artery

Superior cerebellar artery

Circle of Willis

Pericallosal artery

Paracentral artery

Precuneal artery

Dorsal branch to corpus callosum

Parietooccipital branch

Calcarine branch

Medial frontal branches
- Posterior
- Intermediate
- Anterior

Callosomarginal artery

Polar frontal artery

Medial frontobasal artery

Right anterior cerebral artery

Medial striate artery

Medial occipital artery (branch of posterior cerebral artery)

Brain Arteries – sagittal view

True or false?

1   Oxygenated blood to the brain passes mainly through the subclavian artery.

2   The brachial artery passes on the medial side of the humerus.

3   The common iliac artery is a branch of the aorta.

4   The internal iliac artery supplies the lower limb.

5   Arterial blood to the intestines is from the superior and inferior mesenteric arteries.

6   The coeliac artery usually supplies the jejunum and ileum.

7   The radial artery is often used to assess the pulse during clinical examination.

8   The ulnar artery is palpable on the dorsum of the wrist.

9   The external iliac artery becomes the popliteal artery at the base of the thigh.

10   The femoral artery accompanies the sciatic nerve.

11   The brachial artery is often used to test arterial blood pressure.

12   To slow blood loss from the forearm, the brachial artery can be compressed against the medial surface of the humerus.

13   The subclavian artery could be compressed against the first rib to control haemorrhage in the arm.

14   There are two arterial arches in the palm of the hand.

15   Renal arteries branch off the aorta above the muscular diaphragm.

16 *The pelvic organs are supplied by the internal iliac artery.*

17 *The femoral artery passes behind the knee joint.*

18 *The penis is supplied by branches of the internal pudendal arteries.*

19 *The pulse in the posterior tibial artery can be felt behind the medial malleolus.*

20 *The posterior tibial artery is palpable on the dorsum of the foot.*

Cerebral aneurysms

An aneurysm is a localised dilation of a vessel wall. When these form on cerebral arteries (usually at junction points), they are called cerebral aneurysms. Cerebral aneurysms may press against nerves and cause neurological deficits, or rupture, allowing blood under pressure to force its way through brain tissue or flood the subarachnoid space (subarachnoid haemorrhage). Haemorrhage into the brain (a type of stroke) can have catastrophic effects and lead to sudden death or permanent disability.

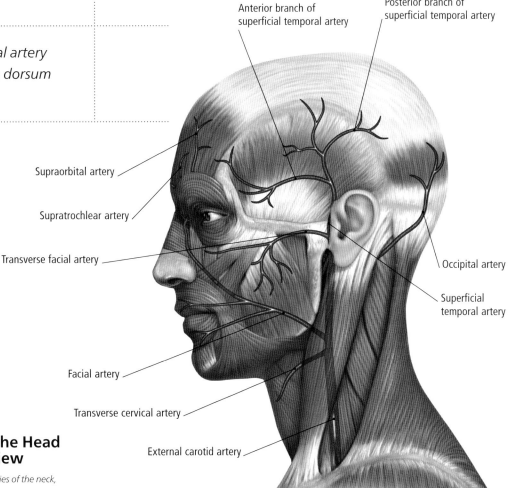

Anterior branch of superficial temporal artery

Posterior branch of superficial temporal artery

Supraorbital artery

Supratrochlear artery

Transverse facial artery

Occipital artery

Superficial temporal artery

Facial artery

Transverse cervical artery

External carotid artery

Surface Arteries of the Head and Neck – lateral view

The carotid arteries are the main arteries of the neck, receiving their supply from the aorta. They supply blood to the neck and its structures, as well as the brain, face, and head via the branches of the carotid arteries.

Multiple choice

1 Which of the following arteries lies along the thumb side of the upper limb?

(A) ulnar artery
(B) brachial artery
(C) subclavian artery
(D) radial artery
(E) axillary artery

2 Which of the following is a branch of the abdominal aorta?

(A) pulmonary artery
(B) renal artery
(C) right coronary artery
(D) brachial artery
(E) femoral artery

3 Which artery can be felt behind the medial malleolus of the ankle?

(A) femoral artery
(B) popliteal artery
(C) posteror tibial artery
(D) dorsalis pedis artery
(E) anterior tibial artery

4 Which artery could be lacerated in a fracture of the middle of the humerus?

(A) brachial artery
(B) radial artery
(C) ulnar artery
(D) subclavian artery
(E) axillary artery

5 Which artery is most important for the supply of the organs of the pelvis?

(A) external iliac artery
(B) obturator artery
(C) femoral artery
(D) renal artery
(E) internal iliac artery

6 Which of the following is a direct branch of the thoracic aorta?

(A) axillary artery
(B) left subclavian artery
(C) right subclavian artery
(D) right common carotid artery
(E) internal carotid artery

7 Which of the following is the first branch of the aorta after the coronary arteries?

(A) left subclavian artery
(B) first intercostal artery
(C) left common carotid artery
(D) brachiocephalic trunk
(E) pulmonary artery

8 Which of the following arteries supplies the stomach and liver?

(A) superior mesenteric artery
(B) coeliac trunk
(C) inferior mesenteric artery
(D) renal artery
(E) common iliac artery

9 Which vessel would be penetrated by a knife stabbing from the umbilicus through to the vertebral column?

(A) abdominal aorta
(B) thoracic aorta
(C) internal iliac artery
(D) common iliac artery
(E) external iliac artery

10 Which artery would be the main supply to the lower anterior abdominal wall?

(A) subclavian artery
(B) external iliac artery
(C) internal iliac artery
(D) femoral artery
(E) lumbar artery

11 *Which vessel is palpable behind the knee?*
- (A) femoral artery
- (B) iliac artery
- (C) tibial artery
- (D) sciatic artery
- (E) popliteal artery

12 *Which artery could be lacerated in a fracture of the lower shaft of the femur just above the knee?*
- (A) popliteal artery
- (B) femoral artery
- (C) posterior tibial artery
- (D) patellar artery
- (E) dorsalis pedis artery

13 *How does the femoral artery reach the popliteal fossa?*
- (A) by passing through the biceps femoris
- (B) by passing through the adductor longus
- (C) by penetrating the iliotibial tract
- (D) by penetrating the adductor magnus
- (E) none of the above is correct

14 *Which artery can be felt on the top of the foot above the first metatarsal?*
- (A) femoral artery
- (B) popliteal artery
- (C) posteror tibial artery
- (D) dorsalis pedis artery
- (E) anterior tibial artery

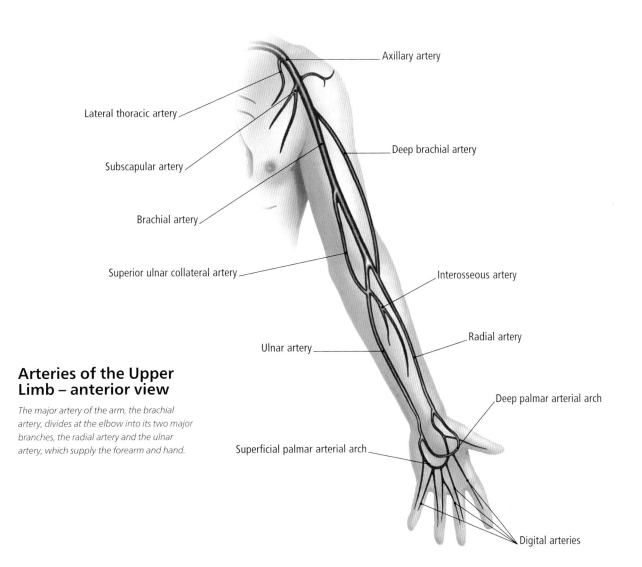

Axillary artery

Lateral thoracic artery

Deep brachial artery

Subscapular artery

Brachial artery

Superior ulnar collateral artery

Interosseous artery

Ulnar artery

Radial artery

Deep palmar arterial arch

Superficial palmar arterial arch

Digital arteries

Arteries of the Upper Limb – anterior view

The major artery of the arm, the brachial artery, divides at the elbow into its two major branches, the radial artery and the ulnar artery, which supply the forearm and hand.

Colour and label

i) Label each structure shown on the illustrations

2 ....
3 ....
4 ....
5 ....
6 ....
7 ....
8 ....
9 ....
10 ....

1 ....
19 ....
18 ....
17 ....
16 ....
15 ....
14 ....
13 ....
12 ....
11 ....

Portal System
– anterior view

ii) Use the key to colour these structures

Liver
Colon
Small intestine

20 ....
21 ....
22 ....
23 ....
24 ....

36 ....
35 ....
34 ....
33 ....
32 ....
31 ....
30 ....
29 ....
28 ....
27 ....
26 ....
25 ....

Arterial System
of Abdomen –
anterior view

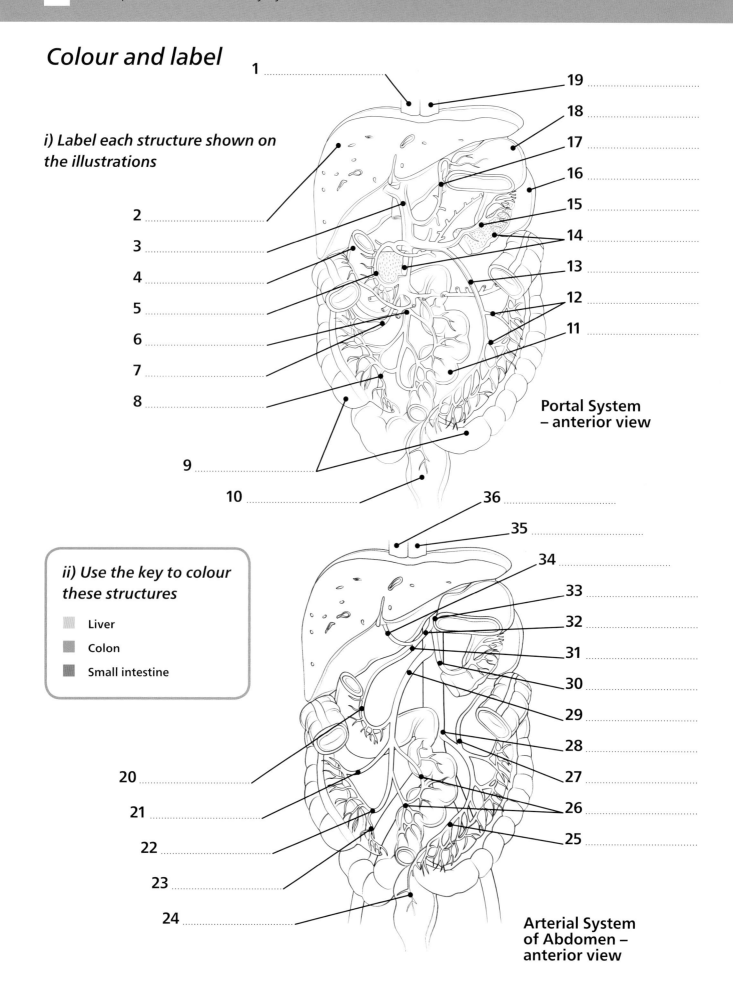

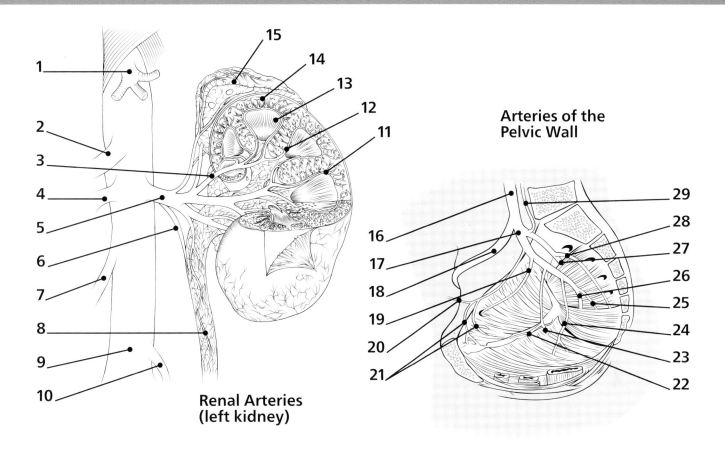

**Renal Arteries
(left kidney)**

**Arteries of the
Pelvic Wall**

i) Add numbers to the boxes below to match each label to the correct part of the artwork

Segmental artery	☐
Ureter	☐
Celiac trunk	☐
Cortex	☐
Left renal artery	☐
Inferior mesenteric artery	☐
Right gonadal artery	☐
Superior mesenteric artery	☐
Interlobar artery	☐
Left gonadal artery	☐
Arcuate artery	☐
Abdominal aorta	☐
Renal pyramid (medulla)	☐
Right renal artery	☐
Left adrenal gland	☐

Obturator artery	☐
Internal iliac artery	☐
Middle rectal artery	☐
Common iliac artery	☐
Obliterated umbilical artery	☐
Superior vesicle artery	☐
Iliolumbar artery	☐
Vaginal artery	☐
External iliac artery	☐
Internal pudendal artery	☐
Superior gluteal artery	☐
Inferior gluteal artery	☐
Lateral sacral artery	☐
Uterine artery	☐

Fill in the blanks

1 The_____is the largest artery in the body.

2 The _____and _____arteries supply the brain.

3 The face and throat are supplied by the _____artery.

4 The right common carotid and right subclavian arteries are branches of the _____.

5 The chest wall is supplied by a series of _____arteries.

6 The posterior abdominal wall is supplied by a series of _____arteries.

7 The arterial supply to the pelvic organs is primarily from the _____ arteries.

8 Arterial supply to the leg and foot is from the _____artery.

9 The _____and _____arteries supply the hand.

10 The gut is supplied by _____, _____and _____arteries.

Arteries of the Lower Limb – anterior view

Blood supply to the leg is provided mainly by the external iliac artery, which becomes the femoral artery as it enters the leg.

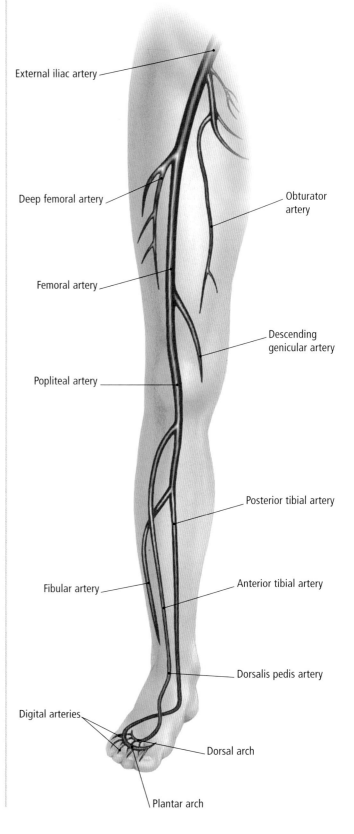

External iliac artery

Deep femoral artery

Femoral artery

Popliteal artery

Fibular artery

Digital arteries

Obturator artery

Descending genicular artery

Posterior tibial artery

Anterior tibial artery

Dorsalis pedis artery

Dorsal arch

Plantar arch

Match the statement to the reason

1   *The pulse can be taken at the groin because …*

a   *both the radial and ulnar arteries supply the forearm and hand.*

2   *Atherosclerosis and blockage of coronary arteries are a prime cause of heart attack (myocardial infarction) because …*

b   *the axillary artery passes close to the humerus in the axilla.*

3   *Obstruction of the radial artery doesn't necessarily cause gangrene of the hand because …*

c   *these arteries supply the brainstem and cerebellum.*

4   *Obstruction of the vertebral arteries can cause dizziness and collapse because …*

d   *the coronary arteries are the sole supply of oxygenated blood to heart muscle.*

5   *A fracture of the upper end of the humerus could cause blood loss because …*

e   *the femoral artery passes under the inguinal ligament here.*

Atherosclerosis

Atherosclerosis is a condition of arteries where there is an accumulation of fatty, fibrous and sometimes calcific material in the vessel wall to form plaques. The material primarily accumulates in the tunica intima, narrowing the lumen of the vessel and increasing the risk of thrombosis on the vessel wall. Thrombosis can cause sudden constriction of the vessel with consequent death of the tissue, e.g. heart muscle, brain tissue. Risk factors include smoking, alcohol, elevated blood pressure, diabetes mellitus and elevated blood lipids.

Veins

Veins are blood vessels that carry blood back to the heart in both the systemic and pulmonary circulations. Systemic veins have valves to facilitate the flow of blood to the heart, and these are particularly prominent in the limbs. Veins are low-pressure vessels and have much thinner walls than arteries, although they also provide an important reservoir function, by storing blood volume in distensible vessels.

Key terms:

Axillary vein The vein of the axilla. It is a continuation of the brachial vein after it has been joined by the basilic vein. It becomes the subclavian vein at the lateral border of the first rib.

Azygos vein Literally the unpaired vein (i.e. there is only one in the body) of the chest. It receives blood from the posterior chest and abdominal wall, and drains into the superior vena cava.

Basilic vein One of the superficial veins of the arm. It runs along the medial side of the forearm and arm to join the deep system at the brachial vein.

Brachial vein The deep vein of the arm. It receives the radial and ulnar veins and becomes the axillary vein at the lower border of the teres minor.

Brachiocephalic vein Formed from the junction of the subclavian and jugular veins in the superior mediastinum of the chest. The two brachiocephalic veins join to form the superior vena cava.

Cephalic vein One of the superficial veins of the upper limb. It runs along the lateral aspect of the forearm and arm to join the deep system at the axillary vein.

Common iliac vein The vein formed from the junction of the external and internal iliac veins. The two common iliac veins join to form the inferior vena cava.

Dorsal venous arch The venous arch on the dorsal surface of the foot. It communicates with the plantar venous arch and drains into the great saphenous vein.

External iliac vein The continuation of the femoral vein after it passes under the inguinal ligament. The external iliac vein joins the internal iliac vein to form the common iliac vein.

External jugular vein The large vein draining the scalp, maxilla, throat, and face. It passes external to the sternocleidomastoid where it may be visible in life.

Femoral vein A deep vein that is the continuation of the popliteal vein. It runs through the femoral triangle, receives the great saphenous vein, and passes under the inguinal ligament to become the external iliac vein.

Great saphenous vein A long superficial vein arising on the medial dorsum of the foot. It passes anterior to the medial malleolus to run up the leg and thigh before entering the femoral vein at the groin.

Inferior vena cava The largest vein of the abdomen. It carries blood from the lower limb, pelvis, kidneys, and posterior abdominal wall. It passes through the diaphragm and enters the right atrium of the heart.

Internal iliac vein The vein that drains the organs of the pelvis and the buttock region. It joins with the external iliac vein to form the common iliac vein.

Internal jugular vein The large vein draining the inside of the skull. It passes deep to the sternocleidomastoid muscle alongside the common carotid artery and vagus nerve.

Median antebrachial vein A superficial vein running up the midline of the forearm.

Palmar venous arch A venous arch draining the digits and palm of the hand.

Plantar venous arch A venous arch draining the digits and sole of the foot.

Renal vein The vein draining the kidney. The left renal vein is much longer than the right and receives the gonadal (testicular or ovarian) and suprarenal veins.

Small saphenous vein A superficial vein draining the skin over the posterior calf. It enters the deep system by joining the popliteal vein behind the knee.

Subclavian vein The vein draining blood from the upper limb. It is the continuation of the axillary vein and joins with the external and internal jugular veins to form the brachiocephalic vein.

Superior vena cava The large vein that drains blood from the head, neck, and upper limbs into the right atrium of the heart.

Vein A low-pressure vessel returning blood to the heart. Veins have a relatively thin tunica media.

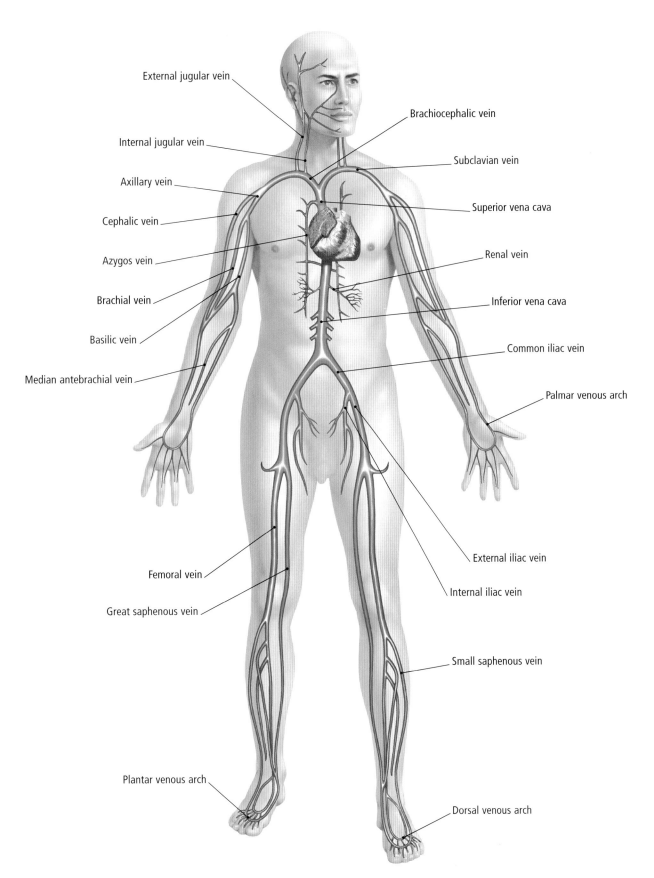

External jugular vein

Internal jugular vein

Axillary vein

Cephalic vein

Azygos vein

Brachial vein

Basilic vein

Median antebrachial vein

Brachiocephalic vein

Subclavian vein

Superior vena cava

Renal vein

Inferior vena cava

Common iliac vein

Palmar venous arch

Femoral vein

Great saphenous vein

External iliac vein

Internal iliac vein

Small saphenous vein

Plantar venous arch

Dorsal venous arch

**Major Veins of the Body
– anterior view**

True or false?

1   The radial vein drains blood from the thumb side of the forearm.

2   The pulmonary veins drain oxygenated blood from the lungs.

3   The great saphenous vein is the longest vein in the body.

4   The short or small saphenous vein runs up the inner side of the thigh.

5   The superior vena cava drains the abdomen.

6   The right testicular vein drains into the inferior vena cava.

7   The portal vein drains blood from the stomach.

8   The left renal vein is shorter than the right.

9   The subclavian vein passes over the first rib.

10   Blood from the brain drains into the internal jugular vein.

Veins of the Lower Limb – anterior view

The venous system of the lower limb includes the great saphenous vein.

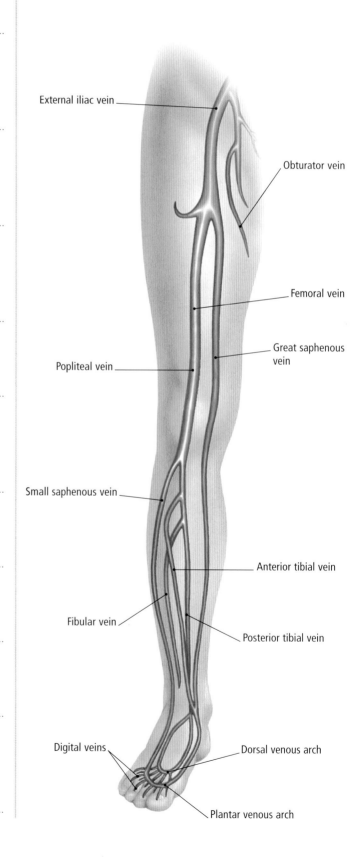

External iliac vein

Obturator vein

Femoral vein

Great saphenous vein

Popliteal vein

Small saphenous vein

Anterior tibial vein

Fibular vein

Posterior tibial vein

Digital veins

Dorsal venous arch

Plantar venous arch

Multiple choice

1 Which vein drains blood from both the head and upper limb?
   (A) inferior vena cava
   (B) superior vena cava
   (C) internal jugular vein
   (D) external jugular vein
   (E) pulmonary vein

2 Which of the following drains directly into the inferior vena cava?
   (A) coeliac vein
   (B) portal vein
   (C) renal vein
   (D) inguinal vein
   (E) popliteal vein

3 Which organ receives the portal vein?
   (A) liver
   (B) kidney
   (C) stomach
   (D) testis
   (E) urinary bladder

4 Which of the following is a superficial vein of the lower limb?
   (A) popliteal vein
   (B) femoral vein
   (C) posterior tibial vein
   (D) obturator vein
   (E) great saphenous vein

5 Which of the following is a superficial vein of the upper limb?
   (A) brachial vein
   (B) radial vein
   (C) cephalic vein
   (D) ulnar vein
   (E) subclavian vein

6 With respect to the veins of the lower limb:
   (A) venous valves are rare
   (B) drainage is from superficial to deep veins
   (C) venous pressure when standing is only a few centimetres of blood
   (D) only superficial veins are present
   (E) none of the above is correct

7 Which vein/s drain blood from the liver to the inferior vena cava?
   (A) portal vein
   (B) superior mesenteric vein
   (C) coeliac veins
   (D) hepatic veins
   (E) phrenic veins

Deep vein thrombosis

Deep vein thrombosis is the formation of a thrombus (coagulated blood) within the lumen of the deep veins of the lower limb. This may occur as a result of venous stasis (slow venous blood flow), for example, when sitting for long periods in an aeroplane or motor vehicle. The patient may experience pain, swelling, redness and localised warmth over the thrombosis. The hazard is that the thrombus may move (embolise) through the veins and obstruct venous return to the heart and lungs. This can cause sudden collapse and death.

Fill in the blanks

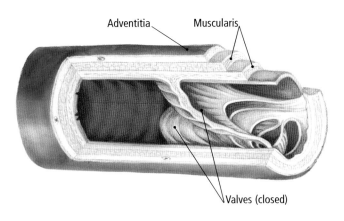

Adventitia   Muscularis

Valves (closed)

Structure of a Normal Vein

Varicose veins

Varicose veins occur when pressure in the veins causes them to dilate and become tortuous. Dilation of veins separates the leaflets of their internal valves so bloodflow can no longer be controlled by the internal valve system. Varicose veins are most common in the lower parts of the body where hydrostatic pressure is highest, i.e. lower limb and pelvis. The effect of elevated pressure is made worse by failure of the valves that channel blood from the superficial unsupported veins of the lower limb to the deep muscle-embedded veins. Once these valves fail, so much blood may pool in the leg veins that the circulation of blood through capillaries of the foot and leg is impaired. Chronic venous stasis ulcers may then develop on the thin skin of the shins.

1   The _____ and _____ drain into the right atrium.

2   Venous blood from the head drains through the _____ and _____.

3   The two largest superficial veins in the upper limb are the _____ and _____ veins.

4   Venous drainage from the kidneys is through the _____ veins.

5   The _____ and _____ veins are the two largest superficial veins of the lower limb.

6   Almost all venous blood from the lower limb passes through the _____ vein.

7   The radial and ulnar veins join to form the _____ vein in the arm.

8   The main deep veins draining the leg are the _____ and _____.

9   Blood from the gut passes through the _____ vein to the liver.

10   Venous blood may be readily sampled from the _____ vein in front of the elbow.

Match the statement to the reason

1   The level of pressure in the systemic venous compartment can be assessed in the neck, because …

a   the external jugular vein is in a position superficial to the sternocleidomastoid muscle.

2   Venous return to the heart is increased by breathing in deeply, because …

b   contraction of the diaphragm lowers the pressure in the right atrium relative to the inferior vena cava.

3   Blood in the lower limb is channelled from the superficial to deep veins, because …

c   a large uterus can compress the common iliac veins.

4   Blood from the gut drains to the liver via the portal vein, because …

d   nutrients and toxins from the intestine must be processed before they reach the systemic circulation.

5   Varicose veins of the lower limb may develop during pregnancy because …

e   there is a series of valved perforating veins that join the two systems.

6   The thickness of the wall of the pulmonary artery is less than the aorta because …

f   pressure in cranial venous channels is below atmospheric when standing upright.

7   Venous sinuses in the skull could collapse without the reinforcement of tough dural membranes because …

g   pressure in the pulmonary artery is only 20 per cent of that in the aorta.

Colour and label

**Circulatory System
– anterior view**

*i) Label each structure shown on
the illustration*

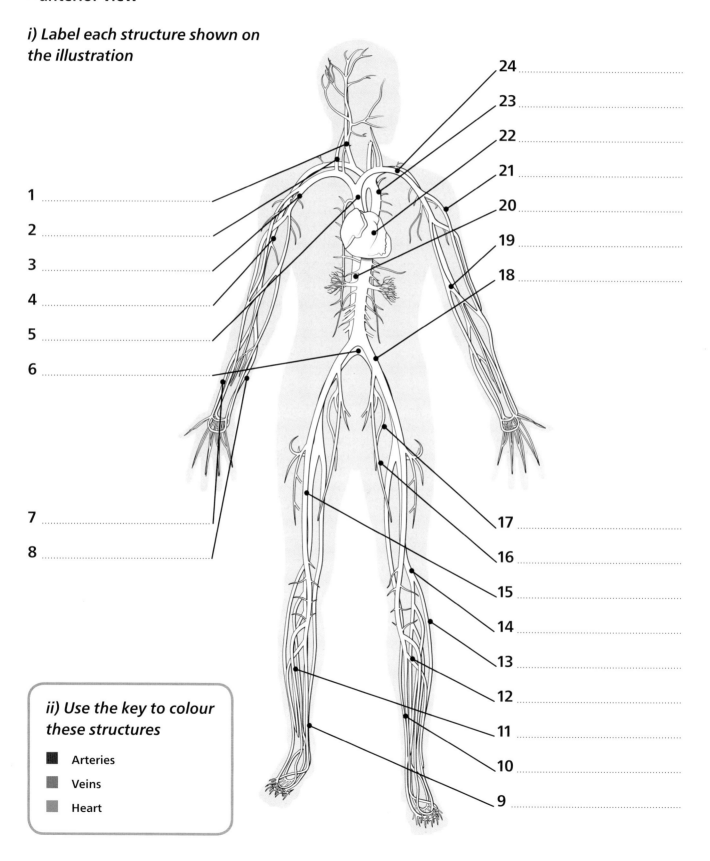

1 ....

2 ....

3 ....

4 ....

5 ....

6 ....

7 ....

8 ....

24 ....

23 ....

22 ....

21 ....

20 ....

19 ....

18 ....

17 ....

16 ....

15 ....

14 ....

13 ....

12 ....

11 ....

10 ....

9 ....

*ii) Use the key to colour
these structures*

■ Arteries

■ Veins

■ Heart

Superficial Arteries of the Head and Neck – lateral view

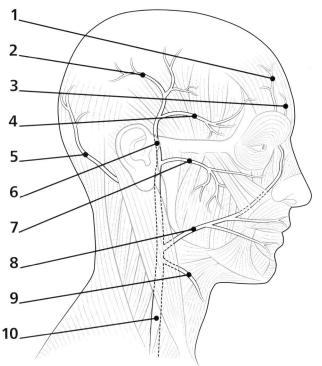

Superficial Veins of the Head and Neck – lateral view

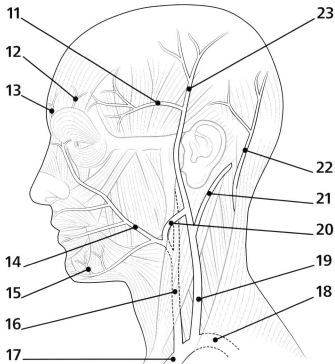

i) Add numbers to the boxes below to match each label to the correct part of the artwork

Occipital artery ☐

Posterior branch of superficial temporal artery ☐

Facial artery ☐

Anterior branch of superficial temporal artery ☐

Supraorbital artery ☐

Superficial temporal artery ☐

External carotid artery ☐

Supratrochlear artery ☐

Transverse facial artery ☐

Transverse cervical artery ☐

Anterior branch of superficial temporal vein ☐

Posterior auricular vein ☐

Supraorbital vein ☐

Brachiocephalic vein ☐

Occipital vein ☐

Internal jugular vein ☐

Subclavian vein ☐

Facial vein ☐

External jugular vein ☐

Retromandibular vein ☐

Supratrochlear vein ☐

Submental vein ☐

Posterior branch of superficial temporal vein ☐

True or false?

1   *Veins have the thickest walls of all vessels.*

2   *Thick-walled arteries often have accompanying vessels called vasa vasorum.*

3   *Arteries have internal valves.*

4   *All capillaries have fenestrations (tiny openings in their walls).*

5   *High-pressure arteries like the aorta have a high content of elastic fibres in their walls.*

6   *The pressure in the femoral vein is higher than in the femoral artery.*

7   *The primary role of systemic capillaries is exchange of nutrients and waste products with body tissues.*

8   *The main role of systemic arterioles is to regulate the flow of blood to capillary beds.*

9   *The tunica intima of arteries has abundant smooth muscle.*

10   *The endothelium is the inner lining of blood vessels.*

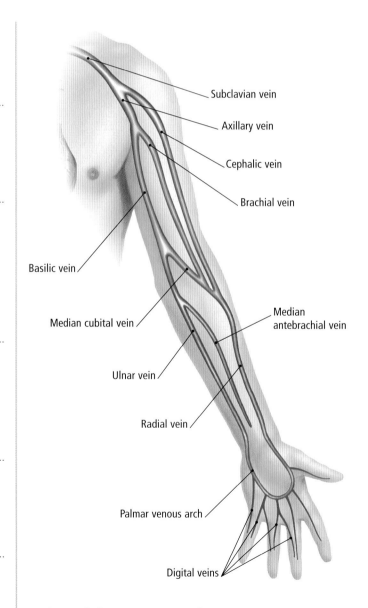

Veins of the Upper Limb – anterior view

The venous system of the arm includes the digital veins of the hands, the cephalic and median vein of the forearm, the basilic vein, and the brachial vein.

Multiple choice

1 *Which vessels provide a capacitance or reservoir function, storing excess blood volume?*
(A) systemic arteries
(B) pulmonary arteries
(C) systemic capillaries
(D) systemic veins
(E) pulmonary veins

2 *Which of the following would NOT be found in the tunica adventitia of an artery?*
(A) nerves
(B) companion arteries
(C) companion veins
(D) lymphatics
(E) mucous glands

3 *The disease atherosclerosis is characterised by fatty and fibrous deposits mainly in the:*
(A) tunica intima
(B) tunica media
(C) tunica adventitia
(D) submucosa
(E) serosa

4 *Which layer of the typical arterial wall has the most smooth muscle?*
(A) endothelium
(B) submucosa
(C) tunica intima
(D) tunica media
(E) tunica adventitia

5 *The main type of cell forming a capillary is the:*
(A) smooth muscle cell
(B) endothelial cell
(C) fibroblast
(D) mucous gland
(E) nerve cell

6 *Fenestrated capillaries are found in the:*
(A) brain
(B) skeletal muscle
(C) skin
(D) lungs
(E) intestines

7 *The thickness of most capillary walls is about:*
(A) 0.1 μm
(B) 1 μm
(C) 10 μm
(D) 100 μm
(E) 1,000 μm

Venous stasis ulcers

Venous stasis (or venous insufficiency) ulcers are areas where the epidermis of the skin is lost due to poor venous drainage. They are commonly found on the shin and ankle of the elderly and arise when the poor drainage of the skin in this region causes inadequate supply of oxygen and nutrients to the tissue. Minor injuries of the skin fail to heal, and these wounds may become infected, forming long-standing ulcers that are difficult to treat.

Fill in the blanks

1   The _____ cells line the interior of all vessels.

2   The thickest layer of an artery is the tunica _____.

3   The valves of veins are extensions of the tunica _____.

4   The elastic fibres of large arteries are mainly found in the tunica _____.

5   The endothelium of capillaries is surrounded by undifferentiated cells called _____.

6   Companion vessels and nerves of large vessels are concentrated in the tunica _____.

7   Capillaries in the intestines have _____ in the endothelium to improve diffusion.

8   The interior of a vessel is called the _____.

9   The elastic layer between the intima and media is called the _____.

10   The elastic layer between the media and adventitia is called the _____.

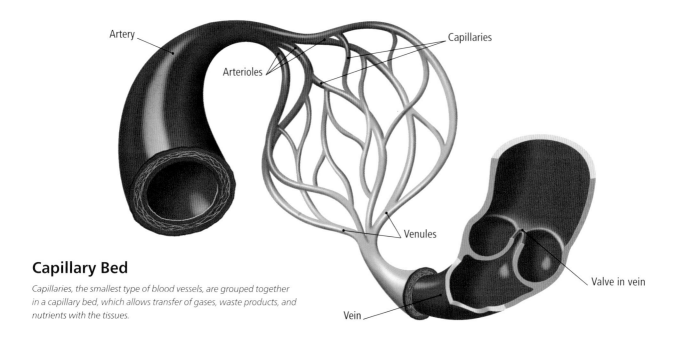

Capillary Bed

Capillaries, the smallest type of blood vessels, are grouped together in a capillary bed, which allows transfer of gases, waste products, and nutrients with the tissues.

Match the statement to the reason

1 *The large systemic arteries of the body (aorta, brachiocephalic trunk, common iliac arteries) contain abundant elastic fibres because …*

2 *The systemic arterioles contain smooth muscle sphincters because …*

3 *The veins of the lower limb contain valves because …*

4 *Capillaries contain only a thin layer of cells because …*

5 *Venules have very little smooth muscle in their walls because …*

a *they need to change diameter to regulate blood flow through systemic capillaries.*

b *they need to allow diffusion of nutrients and gases between blood and tissues.*

c *they are very low-pressure vessels.*

d *they need to expand when the heart pumps out blood and recoil between beats.*

e *they need to direct blood back to the heart against gravity.*

Fenestrated Capillary

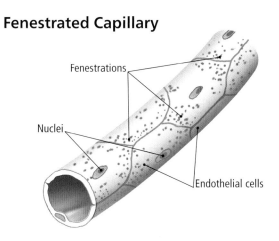

Fenestrations

Nuclei

Endothelial cells

Continuous Capillary

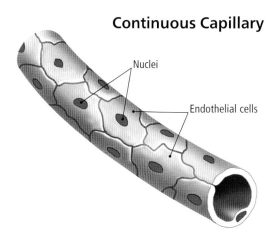

Nuclei

Endothelial cells

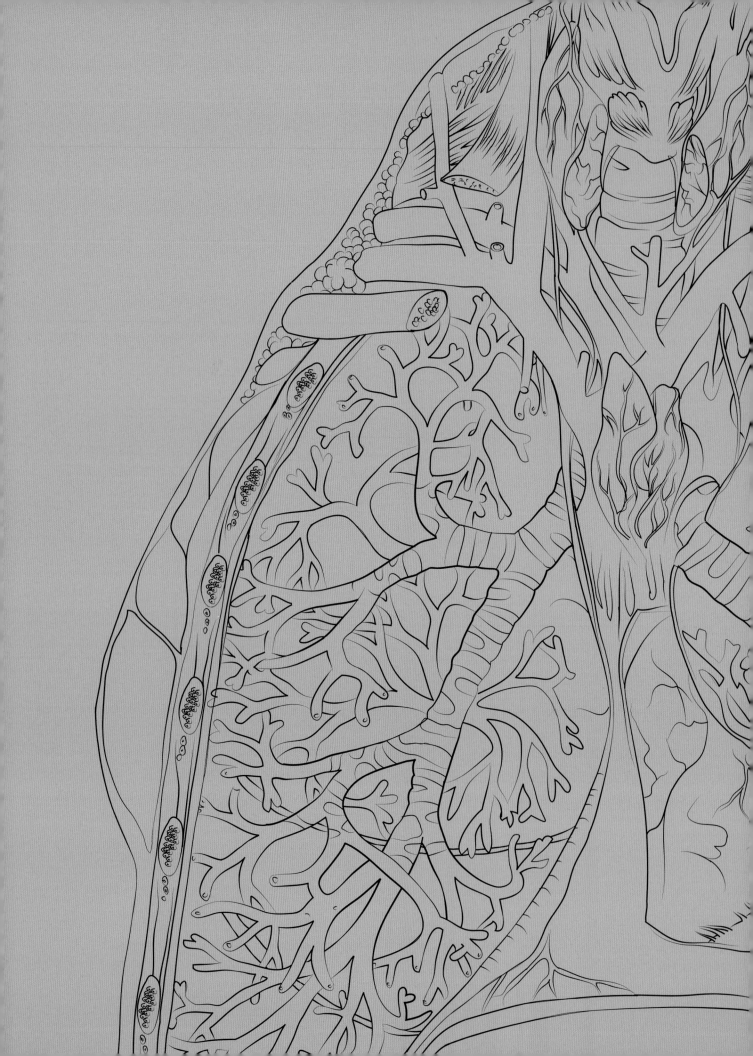

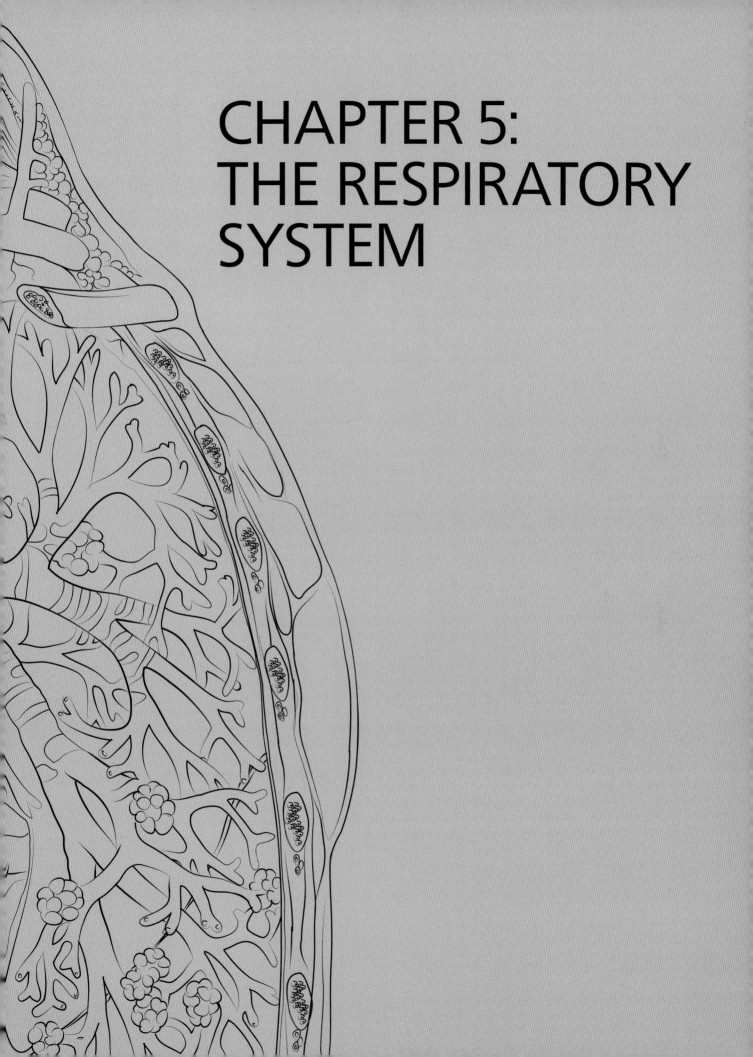

CHAPTER 5:
THE RESPIRATORY SYSTEM

The Respiratory System

The respiratory system is concerned primarily with gas exchange between the blood stream and the external air, although it also serves additional functions such as communication, immune surveillance, acid/base regulation and thermoregulation. The respiratory tract is usually divided into an upper part (nose, paranasal sinuses, and larynx) and a lower part (trachea, bronchi, lungs and pleura). Other critically important structures are the respiratory muscles and the thoracic cage that those muscles move.

Key terms:

Diaphragm A sheet of muscle and tendon separating the thoracic and abdominal cavities. It is perforated by the aorta, inferior vena cava, and oesophagus.

Larynx The part of the airway where phonation (sound production) occurs. The upper larynx (epiglottis and aryepiglottic folds) also protects the airway entrance.

Left primary bronchus The bronchus for the left lung. It gives off an upper (superior) lobar bronchus and a lower (inferior) lobar bronchus.

Lower lobar bronchus The bronchus for the lower (inferior) lobe of the left (or right) lung.

Middle lobar bronchus The bronchus for the middle lobe of the right lung. It branches from the right primary bronchus.

Nasal cavity The internal nose is divided into two cavities by a bony and cartilaginous septum. Each cavity has three bony elevations (conchae or turbinates) on its lateral wall. The superior part of each cavity has an olfactory region.

Pharynx The vertical tube behind the nasal, oral, and laryngeal cavities. It provides passage for both the airway and gastrointestinal tract.

Right primary bronchus The bronchus of the right lung. It is wider and more vertical than the left primary bronchus and is therefore more likely to receive inhaled foreign bodies.

Superior lobar bronchus The bronchus to the upper (superior) lobe of the lung.

Trachea The airway between the larynx and the tracheal bifurcation into right and left primary bronchi. The trachea consists of 16–20 U-shaped cartilages with the trachealis as its posterior wall.

Upper lobar bronchus The bronchus to the upper (superior) lobe of the lung.

Respiratory System – anterior view

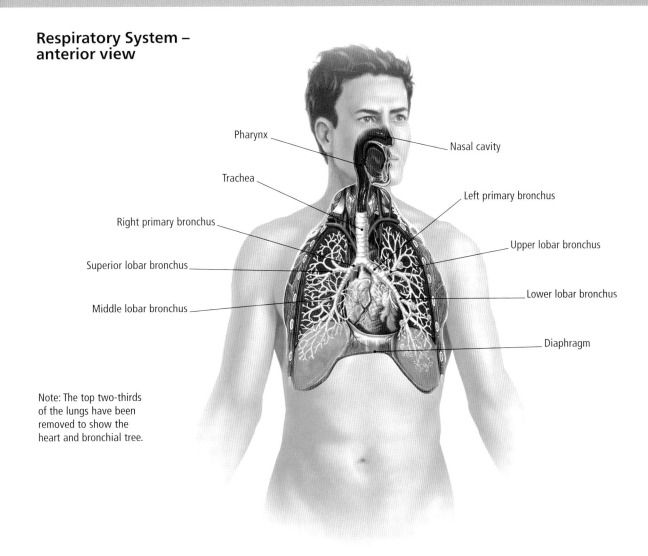

Pharynx

Nasal cavity

Trachea

Left primary bronchus

Right primary bronchus

Upper lobar bronchus

Superior lobar bronchus

Lower lobar bronchus

Middle lobar bronchus

Diaphragm

Note: The top two-thirds of the lungs have been removed to show the heart and bronchial tree.

Upper Part of the Respiratory System – sagittal view

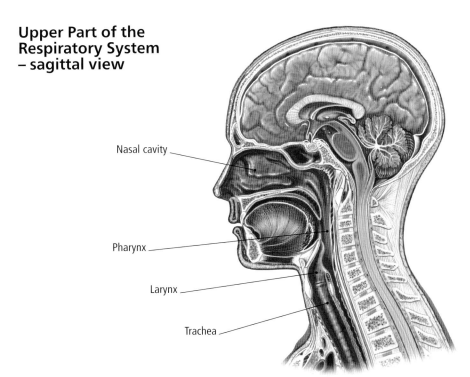

Nasal cavity

Pharynx

Larynx

Trachea

True or false?

1 There are usually four nasal conchae or turbinates on each side of the nose.

2 The initial part of the nasal cavity is the vestibule.

3 The role of the nasal conchae or turbinates is to warm and moisten air and assist with the removal of dust and pathogens.

4 The sphenoid sinus opens into the floor of the nasal cavity.

5 The respiratory part of the nose includes all of the mucosa of the middle and nasal conchae, but only part of the surface of the superior concha.

6 The olfactory region of the nasal cavity lies immediately inferior to the cribriform plate of the ethmoid bone.

7 The typical epithelium of the respiratory part of the nasal cavity is non-keratinised stratified squamous epithelium.

8 The maxillary sinus opens beneath the inferior concha.

Carcinoma of the larynx

Cancer (carcinoma) of the larynx is usually the result of cigarette or pipe smoking. Chronic exposure of the respiratory epithelium to carcinogens will result in mutations that allow epithelial cells to divide out of control. The cancer will produce a growth, which may ulcerate, leading to coughing of blood (haemoptysis), or invade surrounding tissues, causing nerve damage, and spread to lymph nodes and distant sites. Radical surgery is often necessary to remove the tumour.

9 The lateral wall of the nasal cavity contains openings from the ethmoidal, maxillary and frontal paranasal sinuses.

10 The larynx is built around a framework of bones.

11 The laryngeal entrance (aditus) is located in a region called the laryngopharynx.

12 *The rim of the laryngeal entrance is strengthened by the hyoid bone.*

13 *During swallowing, the larynx rises, and the epiglottis is pulled inferiorly to close the laryngeal entrance.*

14 *The vocal fold is the most superior of the internal folds of the larynx.*

15 *The sound of the voice (phonation) is produced by vibration of the vestibular folds of the larynx.*

16 *The vocal folds are moved by rotation of the cuneiform cartilages.*

17 *The vocal folds are lubricated during speech by fluid that drips from the oropharynx.*

18 *The inferior part of the larynx is encircled by the epiglottis.*

19 *The airway passes through the centre of a ring-like cartilage called the cricoid to reach the trachea.*

20 *The muscles of the larynx are all supplied by the hypoglossal nerve.*

Nasopharynx

Oropharynx

Larynx

Laryngopharynx

Trachea

Oesophagus

Location of the Larynx

The larynx lies in the front section of the neck, below the hyoid bone and in front of the laryngopharynx.

Multiple choice

1   Which of the following would be found in or on the epithelium of the respiratory region of the nasal cavity?

(A)   cilia
(B)   pseudo-stratified columnar cells
(C)   goblet cells
(D)   mucus
(E)   all of the above

2   Which of the following opens into the meatus inferior to the inferior concha?

(A)   anterior ethmoidal air cells (paranasal sinuses)
(B)   sphenoidal paranasal sinus
(C)   frontal paranasal sinus
(D)   nasolacrimal duct
(E)   maxillary paranasal sinus

3   Which of the following structures make up most of the nasal septum?

(A)   maxillary crest and plate and frontal bones
(B)   perpendicular plate of palatine and inferior concha
(C)   vomer bone and perpendicular plate of the ethmoid bone
(D)   maxillary crest and perpendicular plate of palatine bone
(E)   vertical plates of sphenoid and frontal bones

4   Which of the following make up the floor of the nasal cavity?

(A)   maxilla and palatine horizontal plate
(B)   sphenoid and maxilla bones
(C)   ethmoid and palatine bones
(D)   frontal and nasal bones
(E)   occipital and temporal bones

5   Inhaled nasal air is under direct surveillance from which part of the immune system?

(A)   lingual tonsil
(B)   palatine tonsil
(C)   nasopharyngeal tonsil
(D)   paranasal sinuses
(E)   thymus gland

6   Which of the following laryngeal cartilages is most mobile during breathing and speech (phonation)?

(A)   cricoid
(B)   arytenoid
(C)   thyroid
(D)   corniculate
(E)   epiglottis

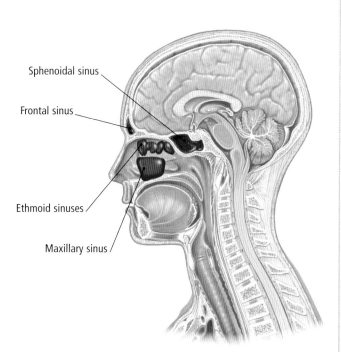

Sphenoidal sinus

Frontal sinus

Ethmoid sinuses

Maxillary sinus

Paranasal Sinuses – sagittal view

The paranasal sinuses are membrane-lined, air-filled cavities in the bones of the skull, which are connected to the nose by passageways.

7   *Which of the following is/are found within the aryepiglottic fold?*

(A)   epiglottis

(B)   corniculate cartilage

(C)   arytenoid cartilage

(D)   both A and B are correct

(E)   both A and C are correct

8   *Which of the following structures contributes to the 'Adam's apple'?*

(A)   cricoid cartilage

(B)   hyoid bone

(C)   arytenoid cartilages

(D)   epiglottis

(E)   thyroid cartilage

9   *Which of the following is associated with the deeper male voice?*

(A)   shorter vocal folds

(B)   longer vestibular folds

(C)   shorter vestibular folds

(D)   longer vocal ligaments

(E)   shorter vocal ligaments

10   *Which of the following structures makes up the core of the vocal fold (vocal cord) of the larynx?*

(A)   epiglottis

(B)   vocal ligament

(C)   cricoid cartilage

(D)   thyroid cartilage

(E)   hyoid bone

11   *Which structures are most likely to be affected by spread of tumour from a carcinoma (cancer) of the larynx?*

(A)   cervical spinal cord

(B)   postvertebral muscles

(C)   cervical lymph nodes

(D)   soft palate

(E)   trachea

Sinusitis

Sinusitis is inflammation of the paranasal sinuses. This usually occurs following an upper respiratory tract infection, when a large amount of mucus is produced by the respiratory epithelium of the paranasal sinuses and nasal cavity. If this mucus thickens, drainage from the sinuses is impaired and the pressure alone can cause pain. If there is an additional bacterial infection, then the pain may become intense. Pain will be felt over the forehead (frontal sinus), the cheeks (maxillary sinus) or centrally in the head (ethmoid and sphenoidal sinuses). Treatment is by nasal decongestants and antibiotics if there is bacterial infection.

12   *Which type of epithelium is found in the larynx?*

(A)   pseudo-stratified ciliated columnar epithelium with goblet cells

(B)   keratinised stratified squamous epithelium with glands

(C)   non-keratinised stratified squamous epithelium with goblet cells

(D)   simple columnar epithelium with submucosal glands

(E)   transitional uroepithelium with goblet cells and mucus

13   *Which of the following describes what happens during whispering?*

(A)   both vocal folds are wide apart

(B)   both vocal folds are completely together

(C)   one vocal fold is in the midline and the other to the side

(D)   anterior vocal folds are separated, but posterior folds are together in the midline

(E)   posterior vocal folds are separated, but anterior folds are together in the midline

Colour and label

i) Label each structure shown on the illustrations

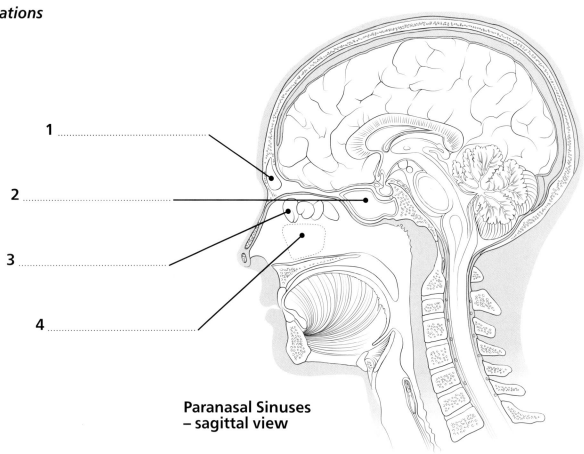

1 ....

2 ....

3 ....

4 ....

**Paranasal Sinuses
– sagittal view**

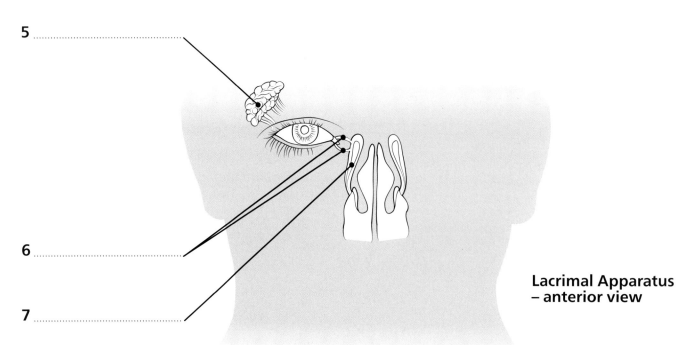

5 ....

6 ....

7 ....

**Lacrimal Apparatus
– anterior view**

Pharynx – posterior view

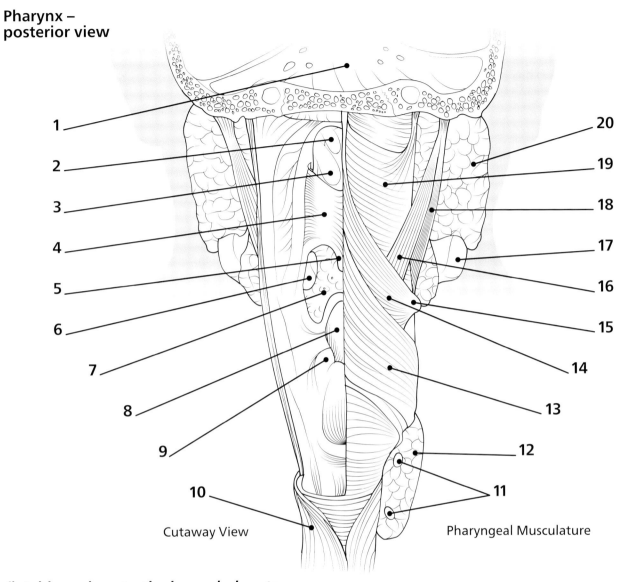

Cutaway View

Pharyngeal Musculature

i) Add numbers to the boxes below to match each label to the correct part of the artwork

Uvula ☐	Parathyroid glands ☐
Inferior nasal concha ☐	Thyroid gland (lateral lobe) ☐
Middle nasal concha ☐	Dorsum of tongue ☐
Soft palate ☐	Epiglottis ☐
Base of skull ☐	End of greater horn of hyoid bone ☐
Palatine tonsil ☐	Stylohyoid muscle ☐
Angle of mandible ☐	Inferior constrictor muscle ☐
Aryepiglottic fold ☐	Stylopharyngeus muscle ☐
Parotid gland ☐	Superior constrictor muscle ☐
Oesophagus ☐	Middle constrictor muscle ☐

Fill in the blanks

1   *The nasal lining is classified as _____ tissue because it contains numerous vascular spaces that can become filled with blood under appropriate stimulation.*

2   *The frontal paranasal sinus opens into the anterior part of the _____.*

3   *Neurosurgeons operating on the pituitary can reach it through the _____ paranasal sinus.*

4   *The maxillary paranasal sinus opens into the nasal cavity inferior to the _____.*

5   *The part of the nasal cavity where hair grows during middle and old age is the nasal _____.*

6   *The upper part of the laryngeal cavity (superior to the vestibular folds) is known as the laryngeal _____.*

7   *Loss of the voice during laryngitis is due to inflammation of the _____.*

8   *The two key functions of the larynx are _____ and _____.*

9   *The three cartilages that strengthen the rim of the laryngeal entrance are the _____.*

10   *The _____ bone protects the upper airway by preventing collapse during deep inhalation.*

Greater horn of hyoid bone

Epiglottis

Thyrohyoid membrane

Thyroid cartilage

Cricothyroid muscle

Cricoid cartilage

Tracheal cartilages

Trachea

Larynx – anterior view

The larynx is composed of cartilages that are joined by ligaments, and held in place and controlled by skeletal muscles.

Match the statement to the reason

1 *Blowing the nose draws mucus from the paranasal sinuses because …*

a *mucus builds up in the frontal and maxillary paranasal sinuses, raising pressure on the sensitive sinus mucosa and providing a rich culture medium for bacterial infection.*

2 *Nasal mucosa is prone to bleeding because …*

b *the pathways for food, fluids and air pass through the upper part of the laryngopharynx posterior to the laryngeal entrance.*

3 *Excess mucus generated during an upper respiratory tract infection can cause pain in the medial forehead and cheek because …*

c *it contains a plexus of large, delicately walled veins.*

4 *Humans are prone to choking during eating and drinking because …*

d *rapid flow of air through the narrow parts of the nose lowers the pressure at the sinus openings by the Venturi effect.*

5 *Phonation (voice production) always occurs during breathing out (expiration) because …*

e *expired air must be forced through a gap between the vocal folds to produce vibration.*

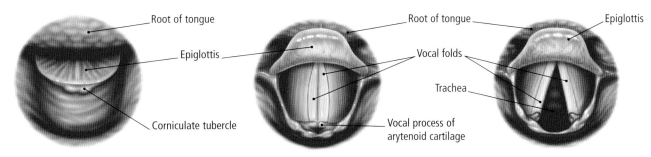

Epiglottis – Swallowing   **Epiglottis – Speaking**   **Epiglottis – Breathing In**

The Lungs

The trachea leads from the larynx to the tracheal bifurcation, where the two main bronchi branch to each lung. Altogether there are about 23 generations of branching of the airways until the alveoli are reached. These last are the main sites of gas exchange, where oxygen from inhaled air is taken up by the blood, and carbon dioxide is released to be exhaled. The pleural sacs surround the lungs and allow free movement of the lungs during ventilation.

Key terms:

Aortic arch See pp. 122–3.

Brachial plexus A network of nerves formed from spinal nerves cervical 5 to thoracic 1 to supply the upper limb. Major nerves arising from the brachial plexus are the radial, ulnar, median, axillary (circumflex), and musculocutaneous.

Cardiac branch of vagus nerve A branch of the vagus nerve that runs to the cardiac plexus. It reduces the spontaneous rate of the sinuatrial node to lower heart rate.

Common carotid artery See pp. 134–5.

Costodiaphragmatic recess A recess in the pleural sac between the costal and diaphragmatic parietal pleura. It accommodates the inferior border of the lung during deep inspiration.

Cricoid cartilage One of the laryngeal cartilages. It forms a ring around the airway and provides a foundation on which the arytenoid cartilages sit.

Cricothyroid muscle A muscle that tilts the thyroid cartilage down, or the cricoid cartilage up, depending on which is fixed by other muscles. It tenses the vocal ligaments and folds.

Diaphragm See pp. 160–1.

External jugular vein See pp. 146–7.

First rib The first rib is an atypical rib. It has only a single facet on its head. It has impressions on its upper surface for the subclavian vein and artery, and a tubercle for attachment of the scalenus anterior muscle.

Inferior thyroid vein One of the veins draining the thyroid gland. It is quite variable in its course, but often enters the brachiocephalic vein.

Internal jugular vein The large vein draining the inside of the skull. It passes deep to the sternocleidomastoid muscle alongside the common carotid artery and vagus nerve.

Internal thoracic vein A vein draining the anterior chest wall. It runs alongside the internal thoracic artery to enter the brachiocephalic or subclavian vein.

Left brachiocephalic vein See pp. 122–3.

Lower lobe (left lung) Separated from the upper lobe by the oblique fissure, this lobe occupies the lung base and back. Its inferior border sits within the costodiaphragmatic recess.

Lower lobe (right lung) The lower lobe of the right lung lies immediately over the diaphragm and the liver. It is bordered above by the oblique fissure.

Lungs Paired organs for gas exchange between the blood and the external environment. They lie within the pleural sacs of the thoracic cavity.

Middle lobe (right lung) Lying against the front of the chest, this lobe is separated from the upper and lower lobes by the horizontal and oblique fissures, respectively.

Pectoralis major A muscle arising from the medial clavicle and upper six costal cartilages to insert into the crest of the greater tubercle of the humerus. It adducts, medially rotates, and flexes the arm.

Pericardium A multilayered sac that encloses the heart. The outermost fibrous layer anchors the heart to adjacent structures. The inner, serous double layer provides a fluid-filled space to reduce friction during beating of the heart.

Right atrium See pp. 122–3.

Right brachiocephalic vein See pp. 122–3.

Right ventricle See pp. 122–3.

Scalenus anterior Muscle arising from the transverse processes of the lower cervical vertebrae (3–6); inserts into the first rib.

Subclavian artery and vein See pp. 134–5.

Superior vena cava See pp. 122–3.

Thymus A lymphoid organ in the anterior mediastinum of the chest. It is active before puberty to produce T lymphocytes, but becomes a fatty-fibrous remnant in adult life.

Thyroid gland A gland that concentrates iodine from the blood to produce the hormones thyroxine and tri-iodothyronine for regulation of the body's metabolic rate.

Trachea See pp. 160–1.

Upper lobe (left lung) The upper lobe of the left lung extends from the left apex to the oblique fissure of the left lung. Sounds from it can be heard over the left anterior chest.

Upper lobe (right lung) The upper lobe of the right lung is in contact with the anterior chest wall. It is bordered below by the horizontal or transverse fissure and behind by the oblique fissure.

Lungs – anterior view

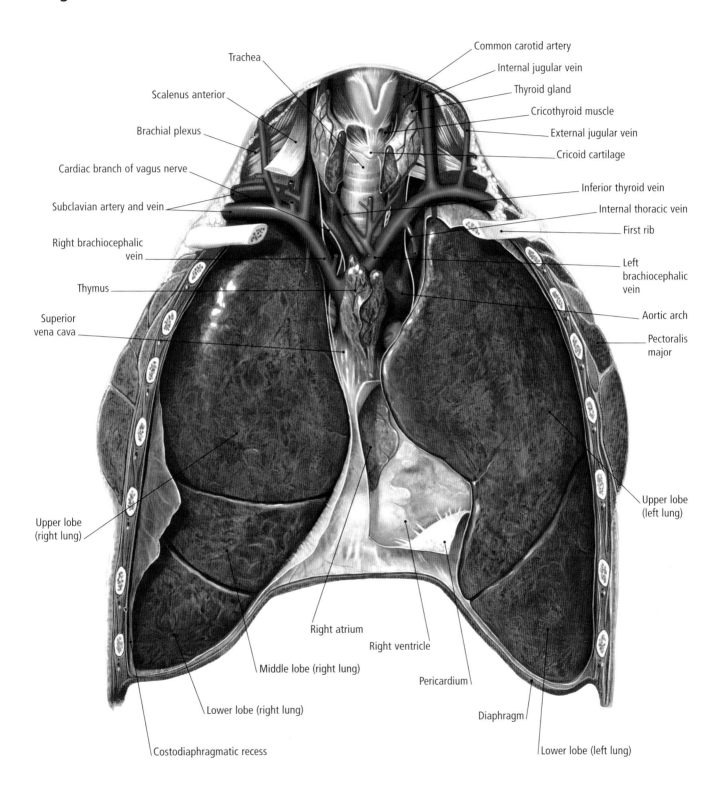

Trachea

Common carotid artery

Internal jugular vein

Scalenus anterior

Thyroid gland

Cricothyroid muscle

Brachial plexus

External jugular vein

Cricoid cartilage

Cardiac branch of vagus nerve

Inferior thyroid vein

Internal thoracic vein

Subclavian artery and vein

First rib

Right brachiocephalic vein

Left brachiocephalic vein

Thymus

Superior vena cava

Aortic arch

Pectoralis major

Upper lobe (left lung)

Upper lobe (right lung)

Right atrium

Right ventricle

Middle lobe (right lung)

Pericardium

Lower lobe (right lung)

Diaphragm

Costodiaphragmatic recess

Lower lobe (left lung)

True or false?

1   *The trachea consists of 16 to 20 continuous cartilage rings.*

2   *The posterior surface of the trachea is made up of dense connective tissue.*

3   *The tracheal bifurcation has an internal ridge (the carina) that is highly sensitive to contact with inhaled foreign bodies and elicits a cough reflex when touched.*

4   *The right main bronchus is usually more vertical than the left.*

5   *The surface of each lung is covered by a smooth, glistening layer called the parietal pleura.*

6   *The division of the trachea into bronchi is at about the level of the manubriosternal joint.*

7   *The pleural cavity is filled with a fluid film that allows free movement of the lung within the chest cavity.*

8   *The normal volume of pleural fluid is about 250 ml.*

9   *The right lung is usually divided into three lobes by horizontal (transverse) and oblique fissures.*

10   *The number of lobes is always a good indicator of which side the lung belongs.*

11   *The two lobes of the left lung are usually separated by a horizontal (transverse) fissure.*

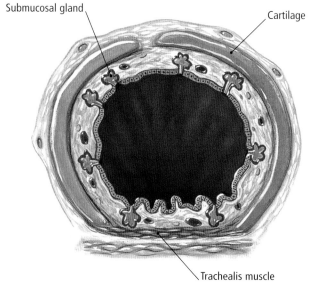

Submucosal gland

Cartilage

Trachealis muscle

Trachea – cross-section

The muscular fibroelastic tube of the trachea is reinforced with cartilage. This flexible tube forms a passageway between the larynx and the bronchi of the lungs.

12 *The horizontal fissure is usually aligned with the sternal angle.*

13 *The surface marking of the oblique fissure of the right lung is given by the course of the sixth rib.*

14 *The inferior border of the lung sits in the costodiaphragmatic recess.*

15 *The anterior border of the right lung is interrupted by a notch called the lingula.*

Pneumonia

Pneumonia is an inflammatory condition of the lungs that mainly involves accumulation of fluid and cellular debris in the alveolar spaces. Pneumonia is usually due to infection with viruses or bacteria. Symptoms and signs include cough with or without sputum, chest pain, fever and difficulty breathing. Risk factors include smoking, asthma, chronic obstructive pulmonary disease and diabetes mellitus. Vaccines are now available against some causative microorganisms, but the condition remains common and serious, particularly in the elderly. Treatment may include support of respiratory function (oxygen), physiotherapy and antibiotics.

16 *There are usually 10 bronchopulmonary segments in each lung, each served by a segmental bronchus and separated from its neighbour by a connective tissue wall.*

17 *The dome of the diaphragm in a standing subject at the end of quiet expiration reaches the height of the 5th costal cartilage.*

18 *The posterior border of the lung lies alongside the vertebral column.*

19 *The apices of both lungs rise above the anterior end of the first rib.*

20 *During deep inspiration, the lungs may pass between the kidneys and the chest wall.*

Multiple choice

1 *Structures in close proximity to the trachea during its passage through the chest include all of the following EXCEPT the:*

(A) left ventricle
(B) oesophagus
(C) arch of aorta
(D) recurrent laryngeal nerves
(E) lymphatic channels

2 *What type of epithelium lines the trachea?*

(A) keratinised simple squamous epithelium
(B) pseudo-stratified ciliated columnar epithelium
(C) simple columnar epithelium
(D) mesothelium
(E) simple cuboidal epithelium

3 *Which of the following contribute/s to clearing the trachea of inhaled debris and microorganisms?*

(A) beating of cilia
(B) goblet cell secretion
(C) tracheal cartilage
(D) seromucous tracheal glands
(E) A, B and D are all correct

4 *Which of the following structures crosses over the left main bronchus?*

(A) arch of aorta
(B) oesophagus
(C) left vagus nerve
(D) left atrium of heart
(E) none of the above

5 *Structures in contact with the right lung include all of the following EXCEPT:*

(A) right atrium
(B) ribs
(C) right ventricle
(D) diaphragm
(E) arch of aorta

6 *The number of times that the airways divide to reach the alveoli is approximately:*

(A) 10 to 14
(B) 14 to 17
(C) 17 to 19
(D) 20 to 23
(E) 24 to 27

7 *What is the approximate partial pressure of oxygen in the lung alveoli?*

(A) 10 mm Hg
(B) 40 mm Hg
(C) 100 mm Hg
(D) 150 mm Hg
(E) 200 mm Hg

8 *Which part of the respiratory tract is NOT part of dead space?*

(A) alveoli
(B) trachea
(C) main bronchi
(D) lobar bronchi
(E) segmental bronchi

9 *The terminal air passages are the:*

(A) alveolar ducts
(B) alveolar sacs
(C) alveoli
(D) respiratory bronchioles
(E) terminal bronchioles

10 *The main role of type 2 alveolar cells is to:*

(A) produce antibodies against invading viruses, bacteria and fungi

(B) produce pulmonary surfactant to lower the surface tension of alveolar fluid

(C) engulf bacteria and inhaled debris, and move these to the lung hilum

(D) participate in gas exchange between pulmonary capillaries and the alveolar air

(E) produce oxygen for the body

11 *Which cell type in the alveoli is primarily responsible for engulfing inhaled foreign material and microorganisms?*

(A) alveolar macrophage

(B) type 1 pneumocyte

(C) alveolar epithelial cell

(D) type 2 pneumocyte

(E) goblet cell

12 *Alveolar macrophages that have ingested soot may migrate to the:*

(A) oesophagus

(B) hilar lymph nodes

(C) larynx

(D) parietal pleura

(E) heart

Pneumothorax

Pressure within the pleural sac is normally below atmospheric. This allows chest wall movement to draw out and inflate the lungs without any direct physical attachment between the lungs and chest wall. The pleural cavity also contains a thin film of fluid, which lubricates lung movement. If the chest or lung covering is punctured, air can enter the pleural sac, and the pleural pressure equilibrates with the external atmosphere (pneumothorax). The lung will then collapse, and effective ventilation is lost. If a flap valve develops, pressure in the pleural sac may even exceed the atmosphere (a tension pneumothorax), and the patient may die quickly from loss of lung ventilation and impaired venous return to the heart.

13 *Haemothorax is the clinical term for which of the following?*

(A) air in the pleural sac

(B) blood in the segmental bronchi

(C) pus in the pleural sac

(D) blood in the trachea

(E) blood in the pleural sac

14 *What is the approximate distance across which alveolar oxygen must diffuse to reach the capillary blood?*

(A) less than 0.1 μm

(B) 1 to 2 μm

(C) 5 to 10 μm

(D) 10 to 100 μm

(E) 1 mm

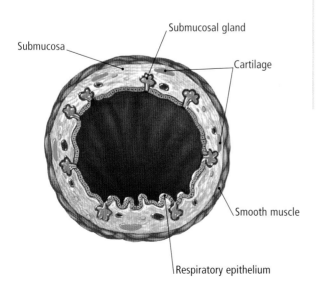

Submucosal gland

Submucosa

Cartilage

Smooth muscle

Respiratory epithelium

Bronchus – cross-section

The bronchi carry air from the trachea to the lungs. The two main bronchi divide into lobar bronchi, which then subdivide into smaller bronchi and bronchioles, which finally terminate at the tiny air sacs of the alveoli.

Colour and label

i) Colour the trachea red and the inferior lobal bronchi blue

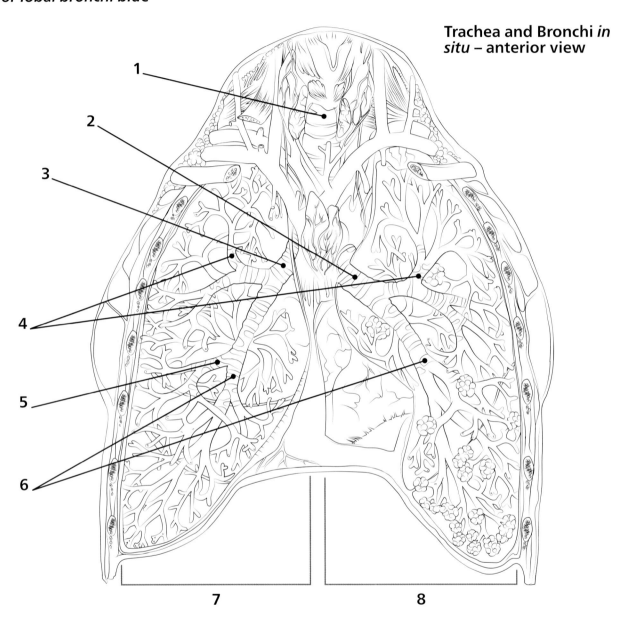

Trachea and Bronchi *in situ* – anterior view

1

2

3

4

5

6

7

8

ii) Add numbers to the boxes below to match each label to the correct part of the artwork

Right primary bronchus	☐	Middle lobar bronchus	☐
Left primary bronchus	☐	Right lung	☐
Trachea	☐	Inferior lobar bronchi	☐
Left lung	☐	Superior lobar bronchi	☐

i) Label each structure shown on the illustrations

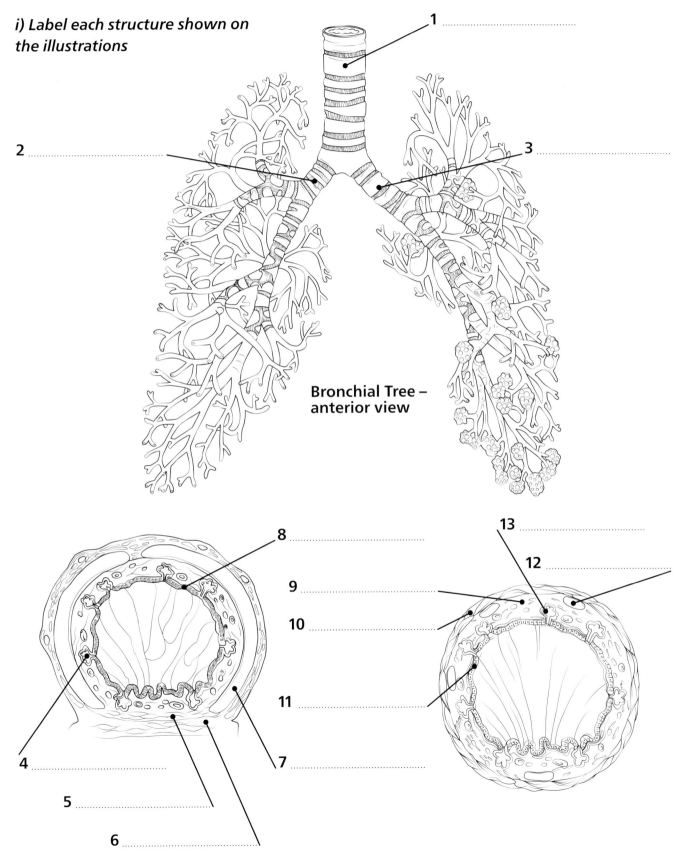

1 ....

2 ....

3 ....

Bronchial Tree – anterior view

8 ....

9 ....

10 ....

11 ....

13 ....

12 ....

4 ....

5 ....

6 ....

7 ....

Trachea – cross-sectional view

Bronchus – cross-sectional view

Fill in the blanks

1   The _____ muscle is the sheet of smooth muscle that forms the posterior wall of the trachea.

2   The _____ lies immediately posterior to the trachea.

3   The _____ is an internal ridge located at the bifurcation of the trachea

4   The two nerves ascending alongside the trachea are the _____ nerves.

5   _____ is a common medical condition where airway smooth muscle contracts, causing airway narrowing and shortness of breath.

6   Most lung cancers arise from the _____ epithelium.

7   Parietal pleura can be divided into _____, _____, _____ and _____ parts.

8   A stab wound to the right posterior chest wall is most likely to penetrate the _____ lobe.

9   The _____ is the tongue-shaped extension of the left upper lobe that passes between the heart and the anterior chest wall.

10   The _____ of each lung sits on the dome of the diaphragm.

11   The _____ is a feature of the anterior border of the left lung due to the extension of the heart towards the anterior chest wall.

12   The _____ is the part of the parietal pleura directly superior to the apex of the lung.

13   The surface marking for the right transverse fissure is a horizontal line that passes through the _____ costal cartilage.

14   *The part of the heart in contact with the right lung is the* _____.

15   *During deep inspiration, the inferior borders of the lungs descend into recesses between the* _____ *and* _____ *pleura.*

16   *The* _____ *are the last generation of the conducting airways.*

17   *Oxygen in the alveoli must diffuse across the* _____, _____ *and* _____ *to reach the blood.*

18   *The* _____ *bronchioles have some alveoli along their walls.*

19   *Lymph nodes of the lower respiratory tract are divided into* _____, _____, _____ *and* _____ *groups.*

20   *The most abundant cell type in the alveolus is the* _____.

Right common carotid artery
Right subclavian artery
Brachiocephalic artery (trunk)
Right brachiocephalic vein
Upper lobe (right lung)
Ascending aorta
Superior vena cava
Horizontal fissure
Pericardium
Right atrium
Visceral pleura
Lower lobe (right lung)

Left common carotid artery
Left subclavian artery
Left brachiocephalic vein
Aortic arch
Left lung
Left pulmonary artery
Pulmonary trunk

Right ventricle
Left ventricle

Lungs and Heart – anterior view

The heart lies in the mediastinum, the region between the two lungs. The heart and lungs work together in the pulmonary circulation, with the two organs connected by the pulmonary vessels.

Match the statement to the reason

1 The posterior wall of the trachea is soft and deformable because …

a the pulmonary arterial blood is too deoxygenated after having passed through the body tissues, and the large airway walls are too thick to allow direct diffusion of oxygen from the airway to the wall tissues.

2 Inhaled foreign bodies are more likely to become lodged in the right as opposed to the left main bronchus because …

b most pathogenic microorganisms (viruses, bacteria, fungi) reach the lungs by inhaled air.

3 The larger airways have their own arterial supply from the aorta (bronchial arteries) because …

c the right main bronchus is wider and more vertical than the left main bronchus.

4 Lymph nodes are located along the major airways because …

d equilibration of pleural pressure with that in the external atmosphere will cause lung collapse.

5 Entry of air into the pleural cavity can have serious consequences because …

e space must be allowed for expansion of the oesophagus inside the bony ring of the thoracic inlet (first rib and first thoracic vertebra) during swallowing.

1 The costodiaphragmatic recesses are potential spaces that are necessary because …

a lung expansion requires a space for the inferior lung borders to enter.

2 Lung markings are more obvious in the lower lobes in an erect chest X-ray because …

b the lung apex passes anterior to the lower roots of the brachial plexus.

3 Lung cancer is most often first seen near the hilum because …

c no alveoli are present in this zone of the airway.

4 No significant gas exchange occurs in the so-called anatomical dead-space because …

d the larger airways have a large surface area in which cancer may be induced.

5 Tumours of the lung apex can cause nerve lesions of the upper limb because …

e blood pools in pulmonary veins when the subject is standing upright.

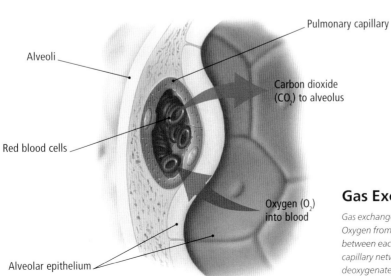

Pulmonary capillary

Alveoli

Carbon dioxide (CO_2) to alveolus

Red blood cells

Oxygen (O_2) into blood

Alveolar epithelium

Gas Exchange

Gas exchange takes place in the tiny alveoli of the lungs. Oxygen from inspired air diffuses through the thin septa between each alveolus to enter the bloodstream through a capillary network. At the same time, carbon dioxide from deoxygenated blood diffuses through the septa into the air sacs, to be expelled from the lungs during expiration.

Colour and label

**Respiratory System –
anterior view**

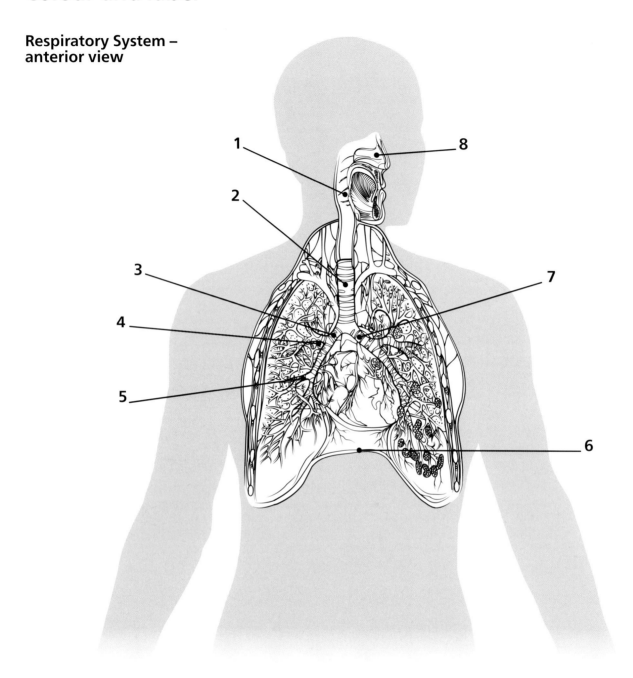

*i) Add numbers to the boxes below to
match each label to the correct part of
the artwork*

Right primary bronchus	☐	Middle lobar bronchus	☐
Trachea	☐	Superior lobar bronchus	☐
Pharynx	☐	Nasal cavity	☐
Diaphragm	☐	Left primary bronchus	☐

i) Label each structure shown on the illustrations

ii) Colour the rectus abdominus muscle in red

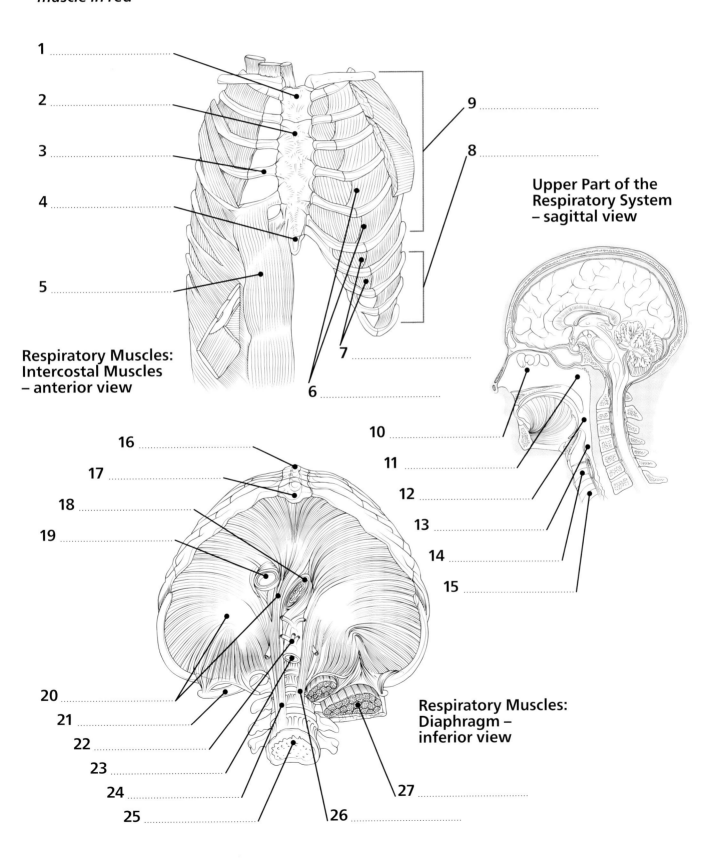

1 ....

2 ....

3 ....

4 ....

5 ....

**Respiratory Muscles:
Intercostal Muscles
– anterior view**

9 ....

8 ....

**Upper Part of the
Respiratory System
– sagittal view**

7 ....

6 ....

10 ....

11 ....

12 ....

13 ....

14 ....

15 ....

16 ....

17 ....

18 ....

19 ....

20 ....

21 ....

22 ....

23 ....

24 ....

25 ....

26 ....

27 ....

**Respiratory Muscles:
Diaphragm –
inferior view**

Answers

pp22–23: 1. True, 2. True, 3. False – The diaphragm separates the thoracic and abdominal cavities, 4. True, 5. False – The diaphragm separates the thoracic and abdominal cavities, 6. False – The dorsal body cavity contains the central nervous system, 7. False – Most of the lymphatic system is a diffuse system of channels and small nodes, 8. True, 9. True, 10. False – The nucleus contains DNA, 11. False – The nucleolus is within the nucleus, 12. True, 13. False – The mineral in bone is hydroxyapatite (calcium phosphate), 14. False – They are covered by hyaline cartilage, 15. True, 16. False – Tubular structure provides maximal mechanical strength for weight, 17. False – The outer membrane of bone is fibrous, not muscular, 18. False – The nervous system acts over milliseconds to minutes, 19. True, 20. True.

pp24–25: 1 – E, 2 – B, 3 – D, 4 – E, 5 – C, 6 – D, 7 – B, 8 – A, 9 – C, 10 – D, 11 – A, 12 – D, 13 – B, 14 – E.

p26: *i) Label each structure shown on the illustrations:*
1. Nucleus, 2. Golgi apparatus, 3. Cilium, 4. Microvilli, 5. Location of chromatin, 6. Mitochondrion, 7. Endoplasmic reticulum, 8. Ribosome, 9. Peroxisome, 10. Nucleolus, 11. Cytoplasm, 12. Nuclear pores, 13. Lysosome, 14. Centriole, 15. Synaptic knob, 16. Axon terminal, 17. Axon, 18. Myelin sheath, 19. Dendrite, 20. Mitochondrion, 21. Nucleolus, 22. Nuclear membrane, 23. Golgi apparatus, 24. Cell body.

ii) Use the key to colour the structures below: refer to i), above, for answers.

p27: *i) Add numbers to the boxes to match each label to the correct part of the artwork:*
1. Red blood cell, 2. Platelet, 3. Cytoplasm, 4. Nucleus, 5. Haem, 6. Globin protein strand, 7. Iron ion, 8. Macrophage, 9. Monocyte, 10. Neutrophil, 11. Lymphocyte, 12. Basophil, 13. Eosinophil.

pp28–29: 1 – D, 2 – C, 3 – E, 4 – C, 5 – A, 6 – E, 7 – A, 8 – D, 9 – E, 10 – B, 11 – A, 12 – D, 13 – C, 14 – E.

p30: *i) Label each structure shown on the illustrations:*
1. Epidermis, 2. Dermis, 3. Subcutaneous fat, 4. Sweat gland, 5. Ruffini endings, 6. Free nerve ending, 7. Nerve ending, 8. Krause bulb, 9. Pacinian corpuscle, 10. Dermal papilla, 11. Deep fascia, 12. Hair follicle, 13. Sebaceous gland, 14. Stratum spinosum and granulosum, 15. Stratum granulosum, 16. Stratum corneum, 17. Hair, 18. Meissner corpuscles, 19. Root of nail, 20. Cuticle, 21. Lunula, 22. Nail.

p31: *i) Add numbers to the boxes to match each label to the correct part of the artwork:*
1. Epidermis, 2. Precuticular epithelium, 3. Internal root sheath, 4. External root sheath, 5. Dermal hair papilla, 6. Nerve, 7. Follicle sheath, 8. Melanocyte, 9. Hair bulb, 10. Internal root sheath, 11. External root sheath, 12. Follicle sheath, 13. Erector pili muscle (arrector pili), 14. Sebaceous gland, 15. Medulla, 16. Cortex, 17. Cuticle, 18. Hair shaft, 19. Skull bone, 20. Pericranium, 21. Loose areolar tissue, 22. Aponeurosis, 23. Skin, 24. Hair follicle, 25. Hair.

pp32–33: 1. brachium or arm, 2. umbilicus, 3. inguinal, 4. antebrachium or forearm, 5. anatomical position, 6. crus or leg, 7. axilla, 8. cervical, 9. popliteal, 10. pollex, 11. pericardium, 12. endocrine, 13. plantar, 14. skin, 15. cubital, 16. ribosomes, 17. axon, 18. chromatin, 19. elastin, 20. collagen.

p34: 1 – C, 2 – A, 3 – E, 4 – D, 5 – B.

p35: 1 – D, 2 – B, 3 – A, 4 – E, 5 – C.

pp44–45: 1. True, 2. False – The hyoid has no direct contact with the vertebral column. The hyoid bone is supported by muscles and long ligaments only, 3. False – There are just 2 pairs of floating ribs, 4. False – The shape of the lumbar vertebrae allows only forward flexion and extension and some lateral flexion, but no trunk rotation, 5. True, 6. False – Only the scapula and clavicle belong to the pectoral girdle, 7. True, 8. True, 9. True, 10. False – The bones of the palm are the metacarpals, 11. True, 12. False – The three components of the hip bone meet at the acetabulum, 13. False – We sit on our ischial tuberosities, 14. True, 15. True, 16. True, 17. True.

pp46–47: 1 – C, 2 – A, 3 – D, 4 – B, 5 – C, 6 – A, 7 – E, 8 – B, 9 – B, 10 – A, 11 – D, 12 – B, 13 – C, 14 – E.

p48: *i) Add numbers to the boxes to match each label to the correct part of the artwork:*
1. Spongy bone, 2. Muscle, 3. Tendon, 4. Epiphyseal plate, 5. Marrow cavity, 6. Bone marrow, 7. Cortical bone, 8. Periosteum, 9. Endosteum, 10. Inner circumferential lamella, 11. Volkmann's canal, 12. Interstitial lamellae, 13. Outer circumferential lamellae, 14. Concentric lamellae, 15. Haversian canals, 16. Trabecula of spongy bone.

p49: *i) Label each structure shown on the illustrations:*
1. Parietal bone, 2. Mental foramen, 3. Mandible, 4. Lower (mandibular) teeth, 5. Upper (maxillary) teeth, 6. Maxilla, 7. Nasal septum, 8. Zygomatic bone, 9. Greater wing of sphenoid bone, 10. Temporal bone, 11. Lesser wing of sphenoid bone, 12. Nasal bone, 13. Frontal bone, 14. Lambdoid suture, 15. Mastoid process, 16. Mandible, 17. External occipital protuberance, 18. Occipital bone, 19. Temporal bone, 20. Lambda, 21. Parietal bone, 22. Sagittal suture.

pp50–51: 1. Volkmann's canals, 2. Haversian canals, 3. periosteum, 4. periosteum, endosteum, 5. cranial vault or brain case, facial skeleton, 6. nutrient foramina, 7. seven; twelve; five; five; three to five, 8. hyoid bone, 9. pelvic or ventral, dorsal, 10. greater, lesser tubercle, 11. trochlear, 12. proximal and distal; proximal, middle and distal, 13. obturator foramen; ilium; ischium, 14. sciatic, 15. iliac, 16. linea aspera, 17. intercondylar fossa, 18. medial malleolus, 19. talus; cuneiforms, 20. talus.

p52: 1 – D, 2 – A, 3 – B, 4 – E, 5 – C.

p53: 1 – D, 2 – A, 3 – E, 4 – B, 5 – C.

p54: *i) Label each structure shown on the illustrations:*
1. Cervical vertebrae (C1–C7), 2. Thoracic vertebrae (T1–T12), 3. Lumbar vertebrae (L1–L5), 4. Sacrum, 5. Coccyx, 6. Cervical region (C1–C7), 7. Thoracic region (T1–T12), 8. Lumbar region (L1–L5), 9. Sacral region (S1–S5), 10. Coccygeal region, 11. Transverse processes, 12. Spinous processes, 13. Axis (C2), 14. Atlas (C1).

ii) Use the key to colour these structures: refer to i), above, for answers.

p55: *i) Label each structure shown on the illustrations:*
1. Body, 2. Transverse foramen, 3. Pedicle, 4. Lamina, 5. Spinous process, 6. Vertebral foramen, 7. Superior articular process (facet), 8. Posterior tubercle, 9. Anterior tubercle, 10. Inferior articular process (facet), 11. Sulcus for ventral ramus of spinal nerve, 12. Body, 13. Transverse process, 14. Pedicle, superior notch, 15. Spinous process, 16. Lamina, 17. Transverse costal facet, 18. Superior articular process (facet), 19. Superior costal demifacet, 20. Body, 21. Inferior articular

process (facet), 22. Inferior costal demifacet, 23. Superior articular process (facet), 24. Lamina, 25. Spinous process, 26. Transverse process, 27. Mammillary process, 28. Pedicle, 29. Vertebral foramen, 30. Body, 31. Inferior articular process (facet), 32. Pedicle.

p56: 1. False – Fibrous joints are the most stable, 2. True, 3. True, 4. False – Ellipsoidal joints allow movement in two axes, 5. True, 6. False – The nucleus pulposus is within the annulus fibrosus, 7. False – It is a saddle-shaped joint, 8. False – The knee joint is bicondylar and allows rotation around the long axis of the femur as well as flexion/extension, 9. True, 10. True.

p57: 1 – A, 2 – E, 3 – E, 4 – C, 5 – E, 6 – C, 7 – D.

p58: 1. Coronal; sagittal, 2. condyle of the mandible; temporal, 3. atlantoaxial or C1/C2 intervertebral joint, 4. atlanto-occipital, 5. parasagittal; flexion and extension; rotation, 6. pronation; supination, 7. flexion; extension; rotation, 8. flexion; extension; medial and lateral rotation, 9. inversion; eversion, 10. talofibular; calcaneofibular.

p59: 1 – E, 2 – B, 3 – A, 4 – C, 5 – D.

pp66–67: 1. True, 2. False – It is the interaction between actin and myosin that achieves the contraction, 3. True, 4. True, 5. False – The correct order is external oblique, internal oblique and transversus abdominis, from outside to inside, 6. True, 7. True, 8. True, 9. True, 10. False – The triceps brachii attaches to the infraglenoid tubercle, 11. False – The biceps brachii also supinates the forearm and flexes the shoulder, 12. False – The triceps brachii attaches to the olecranon of the ulna, 13. True, 14. True, 15. False – Intrinsic muscles are also found in the palm, 16. False –The gluteus maximus is principally a hip extensor. The gluteus medius and minimus are the main muscles for supporting the hip during stance, 17. True, 18. True, 19. False – The gastrocnemius muscle (medial and lateral heads) also flexes the knee, 20. False – There are four layers of muscles in the foot.

p68: *i) Label each structure shown on the illustration:*
1. Sarcoplasmic reticulum, 2. Transverse tubules, 3. Sarcomere, 4. Myofibril, 5. Myosin, 6. Actin, 7. Myosin head, 8. Myosin crossbridge, 9. Actin, 10. Myosin tail, 11. Muscle fibre, 12. Myofibril, 13. Nuclei.

p69: *i) Add numbers to the boxes to match each label to the correct part of the artwork:*
1. Unipennate, 2. Bipennate, 3. Multipennate, 4. Spiral, 5. Radial, 6. Quadrate, 7. Strap, 8. Cruciate, 9. Triangular, 10. Multicaudal, 11. Digastric, 12. Circular, 13. Fusiform, 14. Bicipital, 15. Tricipital, 16. Quadricipital.

pp70–71: 1 – D, 2 – B, 3 – A, 4 – C, 5 – E, 6 – A, 7 – C, 8 – D, 9 – B, 10 – E, 11 – E, 12 – C, 13 – A, 14 – C.

pp72–73: 1. Masseter; temporalis; medial pterygoid; lateral pterygoid, 2. neck flexion; to the opposite side, 3. sternum; ribs; lumbar vertebrae, 4. pubis; ilium; ischium; coccyx, 5. pubococcygeus; iliococcygeus; puborectalis (ischio)coccygeus, 6. pectoralis major; triceps brachii, 7. pronator quadratus; pronator teres, 8. flexion; flexion; supination, 9. biceps brachii; supinator, 10. intrinsic, 11. superficial and deep flexor, 12. hip abductors, 13. adductors; hamstrings, 14. ischial tuberosity, 15. rectus femoris, 16. biceps femoris; semimembranosus; semitendinosus, 17. piriformis; gemelli; obturators; quadratus, 18. adductor magnus; adductor longus; adductor brevis; pectineus; gracilis; obturator externus.

p74: *i) Add numbers to the boxes to match each label to the correct part of the artwork:*
1. Temporalis, 2. Masseter, 3. Scalenus anterior, 4. Scalenus medius, 5. Levator scapulae, 6. Trapezius (cut), 7. Trapezius, 8. Sternocleidomastoid, 9. Sternohyoid, 10. Frontalis.

p75: *i) Label each structure shown on the illustration:*
1. Trapezius, 2. Latissimus dorsi, 3. External oblique, 4. Thoracolumbar fascia.

ii) Colour the trapezius red and the latissimus dorsi orange: refer to i) above, for answers.

p76: 1 – C, 2 – B, 3 – A.

p77: 1 – C, 2 – E, 3 – A, 4 – B, 5 – D.

p84: 1. False – The ascending and descending tracts are in the white matter, 2. True, 3. True, 4. False – Dorsal root ganglion cells are purely sensory in function, 5. True, 6. True, 7. False – The sciatic nerve is the largest nerve in the body, 8. True, 9. False – The ulnar nerve is vulnerable to injury where it runs posterior to the medial epicondyle, 10. True.

p85: 1 – A, 2 – C, 3 – C, 4 – B, 5 – D, 6 – A, 7 – E.

p86: 1. Central canal, 2. grey matter, 3. C5; T1, 4. deltoid; shoulder tip, 5. musculocutaneous, 6. thoracic (T) 1; lumbar (L) 1 or 2, 7. pelvic splanchnic, 8. obturator, 9. saphenous; femoral, 10. tibial, sciatic.

p87: 1 – D, 2 – B, 3 – A, 4 – C.

p88: *i) Add numbers to the boxes to match each label to the correct part of the artwork:*
1. Radial nerve, 2. Median nerve, 3. Ulnar nerve, 4. Musculocutaneous nerve, 5. Anterior interosseus nerve, 6. Digital branches of radial nerve, 7. Superficial branch of radial nerve, 8. Deep branch of radial nerve, 9. Axillary nerve, 10. Common palmar digital branches of median nerve, 11. Superficial branch of ulnar nerve, 12. Flexor retinaculum, 13. Median nerve, 14. Superficial branch of radial nerve, 15. Ulnar nerve.

p89: *i) Add numbers to the boxes to match each label to the correct part of the artwork:*
1. Lateral femoral cutaneous nerve, 2. Femoral nerve, 3. Obturator nerve, 4. Sciatic nerve, 5. Saphenous nerve, 6. Common fibular nerve, 7. Superficial fibular nerve, 8. Deep fibular nerve, 9. Lateral plantar nerve, 10. Medial plantar nerve, 11. Lateral sural cutaneous nerve, 12. Medial sural cutaneous nerve, 13. Tibial nerve, 14. Branches from femoral nerve, 15. Posterior femoral cutaneous nerve.

pp94–95: 1. True, 2. False – The axon transmits information to other nerve cells, 3. True, 4. False – The main neuron of the cerebral cortex is the pyramidal neuron, 5. False – The primary motor cortex is on the precentral gyrus, 6. True, 7. True, 8. True, 9. True, 10. True, 11. False – The corticospinal tract controls the spinal cord motor neurons, 12. False – The caudate and putamen are mainly concerned with motor function and language. The nucleus accumbens and septal area are concerned with reward and addiction, 13. True, 14. False – The sense of smell is processed on the medial temporal lobe, 15. False – Usually language areas are in the left hemisphere, 16. True, 17. True, 18. False – The sympathetic nervous system carries the autonomic motor signals for pupillary dilation, 19. True – this is called prosopagnosia, 20. True.

p96–97: 1 – A, 2 – D, 3 – E, 4 – B, 5 – A, 6 – E, 7 – C, 8 – A, 9 – A, 10 – E, 11 – B, 12 – C, 13 – D, 14 – A.

p98: i) Add numbers to the boxes to match each label to the correct part of the artwork:
1. Frontal lobe, 2. Temporal lobe, 3. Occipital lobe, 4. Parietal lobe, 5. Primary somatosensory cortex, 6. Primary motor cortex, 7. Motor speech (Broca's) area, 8. Auditory association area, 9. Auditory cortex, 10. Wernicke's sensory speech area, 11. Reading comprehension area, 12. Visual cortex, 13. Visual association area, 14. Somatic sensory association area, 15. Central sulcus.

p99: i) Label each structure shown on the illustration:
1. Olfactory bulb (I), 2. Optic nerve (II), 3. Oculomotor nerve (III), 4. Trochlear nerve (IV), 5. Trigeminal nerve (V), 6. Abducens nerve (VI), 7. Facial nerve (VII), 8. Vestibulocochlear nerve (VIII), 9. Glossopharyngeal nerve (IX), 10. Vagus nerve (X), 11. Spinal accessory nerve (XI), 12. Hypoglossal nerve (XII).

pp100–101: 1. Choroid plexus, 2. lateral, 3. cerebrospinal, 4. dural venous sinuses, 5. fornix, 6. corpus callosum, 7. internal capsule, 8. optic chiasm, 9. hypoglossal, 10. oculomotor; trochlear; abducens, 11. lateral geniculate, 12. medial geniculate, 13. middle cerebellar, 14. trigeminal, facial, 15. glossopharyngeal; vagus, 16. central, 17. calcarine, 18. lateral, 19. fourth.

p102: 1 – D, 2 – A, 3 – B, 4 – E, 5 – C.

p104: i) Label each structure shown on the illustration:
1. Thalamus, 2. Choroid plexus of lateral ventricle, 3. Pineal body, 4. Cerebral peduncle, 5. Trochlear nerve (IV), 6. Cerebellar peduncles, 7. Atlas (C1), 8. Second cervical nerve, 9. Spinal accessory nerve (XI), 10. Sulcus limitans, 11. Facial colliculus, 12. Dorsal median sulcus, 13. Pons, 14. Inferior colliculus, 15. Superior colliculus, 16. Lateral geniculate body, 17. Medial geniculate body, 18. Pulvinar, 19. Habenula.

ii) Use the key to colour the structures below: refer to i), above, for answers.

p105: i) Label each structure shown on the illustrations:
1. Spinal nerves C1–C8, 2. Spinal nerves T1–T12, 3. Spinal nerves L1–L5, 4. Spinal nerves S1–S5, 5. Coccygeal spinal nerve, 6. Coeliac (solar) plexus, 7. Peripheral nerves, 8. Spinal cord, 9. Sympathetic ganglia, 10. Aortic arch.

pp110–111: 1. True, 2. True, 3. False – The olfactory tract carries sensory information to the brain, 4. True, 5. False – The taste buds lie within the surrounding trench of each circumvallate papilla, 6. True, 7. False – Olfaction is important for the subtleties of taste, because taste receptors have a limited range of responses (sweet, sour, bitter, salt, umami), 8. False – The lacrimal gland is in the upper lateral part of the orbit, 9. True, 10. True, 11. True, 12. False – The vitreous humour fills the posterior bulb of the eye, 13. True, 14. False – The fovea is lateral to the optic disc, 15. True, 16. False – The middle ear is filled with air, 17. False – The pharyngotympanic tube connects the middle ear with the nasopharynx, 18. True, 19. True, 20. False – The stapedius is important in dampening auditory ossicle movement during loud noise.

pp112–13: 1 – A, 2 – D, 3 – E, 4 – A, 5 – C, 6 – B, 7 – D, 8 – C, 9 – E, 10 – E, 11 – D, 12 – B, 13 – D, 14 – D.

p114: i) Add numbers to the boxes to match each label to the correct part of the artwork:
1. Helix, 2. Pinna, 3. Cartilage, 4. Lobule, 5. External auditory canal (meatus), 6. Temporal bone, 7. Middle ear (tympanic cavity), 8. Eustachian (auditory) tube, 9. Cochlea, 10. Cochlear nerve branch, 11. Vestibular nerve branches, 12. Semicircular canals, 13. Ossicles (malleus, incus, and stapes), 14. Tympanic membrane (eardrum).

p115: i) Label each structure shown on the illustrations:
1. Frontal sinus, 2. Nasal bone, 3. Nasal cartilage, 4. Alar cartilage, 5. Nasal vestibule (nostril), 6. Maxilla (hard palate), 7. Soft palate, 8. Inferior nasal concha, 9. Middle nasal concha, 10. Superior nasal concha, 11. Sphenoidal sinus, 12. Olfactory centres in the brain, 13. Olfactory receptors, 14. Sphenoid bone, 15. Nasal cavity, 16. Olfactory bulb, 17. Frontal lobe of the brain, 18. Olfactory mucosa, 19. Bowman's gland (olfactory gland), 20. Cilia, 21. Olfactory cell, 22. Cribriform plate of the ethmoid bone, 23. Olfactory tract.

pp116–117: 1. Parasympathetic; sympathetic, 2. iris, 3. parasympathetic; accommodation, 4. choroid capillary bed/choriocapillaris, 5. rod; cone, 6. photoreceptors; retinal ganglion cells, 7. fovea, 8. vestibule; bony labyrinth, 9. inner hair cells; outer hair cells, 10. endolymph, 11. auditory tube; acute otitis media, 12. stria vascularis, 13. semicircular, ampullae, 14. high frequency, 15. vestibular; vestibulocochlear, 16. basilar, 17. knob-like endings; cilia, 18. olfactory part of the temporal, 19. nucleus of the solitary tract; insula, 20. chorda tympani; facial.

p118: 1 – C, 2 –D, 3 – A, 4 – E, 5 – B.

p119: 1 – E, 2 – C, 3 – A, 4 – D, 5 – B.

pp126–127: 1. False – The heart is located centrally behind the sternum, but with the left ventricle projecting down and to the left, 2. False – The fibrous pericardium is outside the serous pericardium, 3. True, 4. False – The left side of the heart (left atrium) receives blood from the pulmonary veins, 5. True, 6. True, 7. False – There are two pulmonary veins on each side, 8. False – The muscular wall of the left ventricle is thicker than that of the atria (left or right) because the left ventricle must attain high pressures during systole, 9. True, 10. False – The septum between the left and right ventricles is the thickest wall, 11. True, 12. False – Relatively deoxygenated blood flows through the pulmonary artery on its way to the lungs, 13. False – The mitral valve controls the orifice between the left atrium and left ventricle. There is no valve between left and right atria, 14 True, 15. False – The heart chambers are lined with endocardium. The pericardium is on the outside of the heart, 16. False – The anterior part of the right atrium has muscular elevations on its interior called the musculi pectinati, 17. True, 18. True, 19. False – The left atrium lies at the heart base, 20. True.

pp128–129: 1 – C, 2 – A, 3 – B, 4 – C, 5 – E, 6 – D, 7 – D, 8 – E, 9 – C, 10 – D, 11 – B, 12 – A, 13 – D, 14 – E, 15 – A.

p130: i) Colour the arteries in red, and the veins in blue: refer to iii), below, for answers.
ii) Add numbers to the boxes to match each label to the correct part of the artwork:
1. Brachiocephalic artery, 2. Right brachiocephalic vein, 3. Superior vena cava, 4. Ascending aorta, 5. Right pulmonary artery, 6. Right superior pulmonary vein, 7. Right inferior pulmonary vein, 8. Right atrium, 9. Cusp of tricuspid valve, 10. Right ventricle, 11. Papillary muscles, 12. Inferior vena cava, 13. Descending thoracic aorta, 14. Chordae tendineae,

15. Cusp of mitral valve, 16. Pulmonary valve, 17. Left atrium, 18. Left inferior pulmonary vein, 19. Left superior pulmonary vein, 20. Ligamentum arteriosum, 21. Left pulmonary artery, 22. Aortic arch, 23. Left brachiocephalic vein, 24. Left subclavian artery, 25. Left common carotid artery.

p131: *i) Label each structure shown on the illustration:*
1. Left brachiocephalic vein, 2. Brachiocephalic trunk, 3. Right common carotid artery, 4. Right subclavian artery, 5. Right brachiocephalic vein, 6. Right lung (upper lobe), 7. Ascending aorta, 8. Superior vena cava, 9. Pericardium, 10. Right atrium, 11. Right ventricle, 12. Pleura, 13. Right lung (lower lobe), 14. Diaphragm, 15. Left ventricle, 16. Pulmonary trunk, 17. Left pulmonary artery, 18. Left lung (upper lobe), 19. Aortic arch, 20. Left subclavian artery, 21. Left common carotid artery.

p132: 1. coronary sinus, 2. aorta, 3. apex, 4. muscular, membranous, 5. tricuspid, 6. pulmonary artery, 7. right atrium, 8. ascending aorta, 9. trabeculae carneae, 10. musculi pectinati, 11. right ventricle, 12. left ventricle.

p133: 1 – C, 2 – E, 3 – A, 4 – D, 5 – B.

pp138–139: 1. False – Oxygenated blood to the brain passes mainly through internal carotid arteries, 2. True, 3. True, 4. False – The external iliac artery supplies the lower limb. The internal iliac artery supplies pelvic organs and the buttock, 5. True, 6. False – The coeliac artery usually supplies the stomach, spleen, liver, gallbladder and part of the duodenum, 7. True, 8. False – The ulnar artery is found on the medial palmar side of the wrist, 9. False – The external iliac artery becomes the femoral artery at the base of the thigh, 10. False – The femoral artery accompanies the femoral nerve, 11. True, 12. True, 13. True, 14. True, 15. False – Renal arteries are branches of the abdominal aorta, below the diaphragm, 16. True, 17. False – The femoral artery becomes the popliteal artery at the adductor canal. The popliteal artery lies posterior to the knee joint, 18. True, 19. True, 20. False – It is the dorsalis pedis artery that is palpable on the dorsum of the foot. The posterior tibial artery can only be felt behind the medial malleolus.

pp140–141: 1 – D, 2 – B, 3 – C, 4 – A, 5 – E, 6 – B, 7 – D, 8 – B, 9 – A, 10 – B, 11 – E, 12 – A, 13 – D, 14 – D.

p142: *i) Label each structure shown on the illustrations:*
1. Inferior vena cava, 2. Liver, 3. Portal vein, 4. Duodenum, 5. Pancreaticoduodenal vein, 6. Superior mesenteric vein, 7. Right colic vein, 8. Appendicular vein, 9. Colon, 10. Rectum, 11. Small intestine, 12. Left colic veins, 13. Inferior mesenteric vein, 14. Pancreas, 15. Splenic vein, 16. Spleen, 17. Left gastric vein, 18. Stomach, 19. Thoracic aorta, 20. Pancreaticoduodenal artery, 21. Right colic artery, 22. Ileocolic artery, 23. Appendicular artery, 24. Rectal artery, 25. Sigmoidal artery, 26. Jejunal arteries, 27. Left colic artery, 28. Inferior mesenteric artery, 29. Superior mesenteric artery, 30. Splenic artery, 31. Gastroduodenal artery, 32. Common hepatic artery, 33. Coeliac trunk, 34. Hepatic artery proper, 35. Thoracic aorta, 36. Inferior vena cava.

ii) Use the key to colour the structures below: refer to i), above, for answers.

p143: *i) Add numbers to the boxes to match each label to the correct part of the artwork:*
1. Coeliac trunk, 2. Superior mesenteric artery, 3. Segmental artery, 4. Right renal artery, 5. Left renal artery, 6. Ureteric branch of the left renal artery, 7. Right gonadal artery, 8. Ureter, 9. Abdominal aorta, 10. Inferior

mesenteric artery, 11. Arcuate artery, 12. Interlobar artery, 13. Renal pyramid (medulla), 14. Cortex, 15. Left adrenal gland, 16. Common iliac artery, 17. Internal iliac artery, 18. External iliac artery, 19. Obturator artery, 20. Obliterated umbilical artery, 21. Superior vesical artery, 22. Uterine artery, 23. Vaginal artery, 24. Middle rectal artery, 25. Internal pudendal artery, 26. Inferior gluteal artery, 27. Superior gluteal artery, 28. Lateral sacral artery, 29. Iliolumbar artery.

p144: 1. Aorta, 2. internal carotid; vertebral, 3. external carotid, 4. brachiocephalic trunk, 5. intercostal, 6. lumbar, 7. internal iliac, 8. popliteal, 9. radial and ulnar, 10. coeliac; superior mesenteric and inferior mesenteric.

p145: 1 – E, 2 – D, 3 – A, 4 – C, 5 – B.

p148: 1. True, 2. True, 3. True, 4. False – The long or great saphenous vein runs up the inner side of the thigh. The short saphenous vein ends at the popliteal fossa, 5. False – The superior vena cava drains the head, neck, upper limbs and upper chest, 6. True, 7. True, 8. False – The left renal vein is longer than the right because the inferior vena cava (into which they both drain) is on the right side of the abdomen, 9. True, 10. True.

p149: 1 – B, 2 – C, 3 – A, 4 – E, 5 – C, 6 – B, 7 – D.

p150: 1. Superior vena cava; inferior vena cava, 2. external jugular vein; internal jugular vein, 3. basilic; cephalic, 4. renal, 5. small/short saphenous; great saphenous, 6. femoral, 7. brachial, 8. posterior tibial; anterior tibial; 9. portal, 10. median cubital.

p151: 1 – A, 2 – B, 3 – E, 4 – D, 5 – C, 6 – G, 7 – F.

p152: *i) Label each structure shown on the illustration:*
1. Common carotid artery, 2. External jugular vein, 3. Axillary vein, 4. Brachial artery, 5. Superior vena cava, 6. Common iliac vein, 7. Radial artery, 8. Ulnar artery, 9. Posterior tibial artery, 10. Great saphenous vein, 11. Anterior tibial artery, 12. Fibular artery, 13. Small/short saphenous vein, 14. Popliteal vein, 15. Femoral artery, 16. Obturator artery, 17. Obturator vein, 18. Common iliac artery, 19. Basilic vein, 20. Inferior vena cava, 21. Cephalic vein, 22. Heart, 23. Arch of aorta, 24. Subclavian vein.

ii) Use the key to colour these structures: refer to i), above, for answers.

p153: *i) Add numbers to the boxes to match each label to the correct part of the artwork:*
1. Supraorbital artery, 2. Posterior branch of superficial temporal artery, 3. Supratrochlear artery, 4. Anterior branch of superficial temporal artery, 5. Occipital artery, 6. Superficial temporal artery, 7. Transverse facial artery, 8. Facial artery, 9. Transverse cervical artery, 10. External carotid artery, 11. Anterior branch of superficial temporal vein, 12. Supraorbital vein, 13. Supratrochlear vein, 14. Facial vein, 15. Submental vein, 16. Internal jugular vein, 17. Brachiocephalic vein, 18. Subclavian vein, 19. External jugular vein, 20. Retromandibular vein, 21. Posterior auricular vein, 22. Occipital vein, 23. Posterior branch of superficial temporal vein.

p154: 1. False – Arteries have the thickest walls of all vessels, 2. True, 3. False – Although there are semilunar valves where the pulmonary trunk and aorta arise from the heart, there are no valves in arteries. The high pressure and velocity of flow in arteries make valves unnecessary, 4. False – Not all capillaries have fenestrations. Fenestrations are found where large molecules must cross the vessel wall, e.g. in endocrine glands, intestines, pancreas, 5. True, 6. False – Pressure is much higher in the femoral artery, 7. True, 8. True, 9. False – Smooth muscle is mainly found in the tunica media, 10. True.

p155: 1 – D, 2 – E, 3 – A, 4 – D, 5 – B, 6 – E, 7 – C.

p156: 1. Endothelial, 2. media, 3. intima, 4. media, 5. pericytes, 6. adventitia, 7. fenestrations, 8. lumen, 9. internal elastic lamina, 10. external elastic lamina.

p157: 1 – D, 2 – A, 3 – E, 4 – B, 5 – C.

pp162–163: 1. False – There are usually three nasal conchae or turbinates on each side, 2. True, 3. True, 4. False – The sphenoid sinus opens into the posterior roof region, 5. True, 6. True, 7. False – The respiratory part of the nasal cavity is lined with ciliated pseudo-stratified columnar epithelium with goblet cells, 8. False – The maxillary sinus opens into the middle meatus beneath the middle concha, 9. True, 10. False – The component hard parts of the larynx are cartilaginous, 11. True, 12. False – The laryngeal entrance is strengthened by the epiglottis and other small cartilages, 13. True, 14. False – The vestibular fold is superior to the vocal fold, 15. False – The voice is produced by vibration of the vocal fold, 16. False – The arytenoid cartilages rotate and slide to move the vocal folds, 17. False – The laryngeal saccule provides lubrication for the vocal fold, 18. False – The epiglottis is superior and anterior to the superior larynx, 19. True, 20. False – The laryngeal muscles are supplied by the vagus nerve.

pp164–165: 1 – E, 2 – D, 3 – C, 4 – A, 5 – C, 6 – B, 7 – D, 8 – E, 9 – D, 10 – B, 11 – C, 12 – A, 13 – E.

p166: i) Label each structure shown on the illustrations:
1. Frontal sinus, 2. Sphenoid sinus, 3. Ethmoid sinuses, 4. Maxillary sinus, 5. Lacrimal gland, 6. Lacrimal canals, 7. Nasolacrimal duct.

p167: i) Add numbers to the boxes to match each label to the correct part of the artwork:
1. Base of skull, 2. Middle nasal concha, 3. Inferior nasal concha, 4. Soft palate, 5. Uvula, 6. Palatine tonsil, 7. Dorsum of tongue, 8. Epiglottis, 9. Aryepiglottic fold, 10. Oesophagus, 11. Parathyroid glands, 12. Thyroid gland (lateral lobe), 13. Inferior constrictor muscle, 14. Middle constrictor muscle, 15. End of greater horn of hyoid bone, 16. Stylopharyngeus muscle, 17. Angle of mandible, 18. Stylohyoid muscle, 19. Superior constrictor muscle, 20. Parotid gland.

p168: 1. Erectile, 2. middle nasal meatus, 3. sphenoid, 4. middle nasal concha, 5. vestibule, 6. vestibule, 7. vocal folds, 8. protection of the airway; phonation (voice production), 9. epiglottis; corniculate; cuneiform, 10. hyoid.

p169: 1 – D, 2 – C, 3 – A, 4 – B, 5 – E.

pp172–173: 1. False – Tracheal cartilages are not complete rings, they are 'U'-shaped, 2. False – The posterior wall of the trachea is smooth muscle (the trachealis), 3. True, 4. True, 5. False – The visceral or pulmonary pleura covers each lung, 6. False – The branching of the trachea occurs at the level of the sternal body (thoracic vertebrae 5 to 6), 7. True, 8. False – Normally the pleural fluid is less than 20 ml, 9. True, 10. False – The division of lungs into lobes is variable. The left lung may have a partial horizontal fissure, and the right lung may have an incomplete horizontal fissure in some people, 11. False – The two lobes of the left lung are separated by the oblique fissure, 12. False – The sternal angle is

level with the second costal cartilage, and the horizontal fissure is usually at the level of the fourth costal cartilage, 13. True, 14. True, 15. False – The anterior border of the left lung has the notch, and it is called the cardiac notch, 16. True, 17. True, 18. True, 19. True, 20. True.

p174–175: 1 – A, 2 – B, 3 – E, 4 – A, 5 – E, 6 – D, 7 – D, 8 – A, 9 – C, 10 – B, 11 – A, 12 – B, 13 – E, 14 – B.

p176: i) Colour the trachea red and the inferior lobar bronchi blue: refer to ii), below, for the correct answers.
ii) Add numbers to the boxes to match each label to the correct part of the artwork:
1. Trachea, 2. Left primary bronchus, 3. Right primary bronchus, 4. Superior lobar bronchi, 5. Middle lobar bronchus, 6. Inferior lobar bronchi, 7. Right lung, 8. Left lung.

p177: i) Label each structure shown on the illustrations:
1. Trachea, 2. Right primary bronchus, 3. Left primary bronchus, 4. Submucosal gland, 5. Trachealis muscle, 6. Annular ligament, 7. Cartilage, 8. Respiratory epithelium, 9. Submucosa, 10. Smooth muscle, 11. Respiratory epithelium, 12. Cartilage, 13. Submucosal gland.

pp178–179: 1. Trachealis, 2. oesophagus, 3. carina, 4. recurrent laryngeal, 5. asthma, 6. bronchial, 7. cervical; costal; mediastinal; diaphragmatic, 8. inferior or lower, 9. lingula, 10. base, 11. cardiac notch, 12. cupola, 13. 4th, 14. right atrium, 15. costal; diaphragmatic, 16. terminal bronchioles, 17. type 1 pneumocyte/alveolar epithelium; basement membrane; alveolar capillary endothelium, 18. respiratory, 19. pulmonary; bronchopulmonary (hilar); tracheobronchial; paratracheal, 20. type 1 pneumocyte or alveolar cell.

p180: 1 – E, 2 – C, 3 – A, 4 – B, 5 – D.

p181: 1 – A, 2 – E, 3 – D, 4 – C, 5 – B.

p182: i) Add numbers to the boxes below to match each label to the correct part of the artwork:
1. Pharynx, 2. Trachea, 3. Right primary bronchus, 4. Superior lobar bronchus, 5. Middle lobar bronchus, 6. Diaphragm, 7. Left primary bronchus, 8. Nasal cavity.

p183: i) Label each structure shown on the illustrations:
1. Manubrium, 2. Body of sternum, 3. Costal cartilage, 4. Xiphoid process, 5. Rectus abdominus muscle, 6. External intercostal muscles, 7. Internal intercostal muscles, 8. Ribs 8–10 ('floating' ribs), 9. Ribs 1–7 ('true' ribs), 10. Nasal cavity, 11. Nasopharynx, 12. Oropharynx, 13. Laryngopharynx, 14. Larynx, 15. Trachea, 16. Body of sternum, 17. Xiphoid process, 18. Oesophagus, 19. Inferior vena cava, 20. Central tendon, 21. Twelfth rib, 22. Coeliac trunk, 23. Abdominal aorta, 24. Right crus of diaphragm, 25. Vertebral column, 26. Left crus of diaphragm, 27. Quadratus lumborum muscle.

ii) Colour the rectus abdominus muscle in red: refer to i), above, for correct answer.

Index

A

abdomen 14, 142
abdominal cavity 16
abdominopelvic cavity 16
abductor pollicis longus 62
acromioclavicular joint 40
acromion 38, 40
adductor longus 64
adductor magnus 64
adductor tubercle 42
adipose tissue 20
ampullae 107
anatomical planes 18, 19
anconeus 62
ankle/tarsus 14
anterior border 42
anterior cerebral artery 136
anterior chamber 106
anterior communicating artery 136
anterior corticospinal tract 82
anterior inferior cerebellar artery 136
anterior intercondylar area 42
anterior median fissure 82
anterior nasal (piriform) aperture 38
anterior orientation 18
anterior radicular artery 82
anterior ramus of spinal nerve 82
anterior spinal artery 82
anterior spinal vein 82
anterior tibial artery 134
aorta 134
aortic arch 122, 134, 170
aortic valve 122, 124
apex of fibula 42
appetite regulation 103
arachnoid 82
arm/brachium 14
armpit/axilla 14
arteries 134–145, 153
articular facet for talus 42
articular facet of medial malleolus 42
articular surface with head of fibula 42
ascending aorta 122
atherosclerosis 145
atlas (C1) 38
atrium 122, 124, 170
auditory association area 92
axial skeleton 38–39
axillary artery 134
axillary (circumflex) nerve 80
axillary vein 146
axis (C2) 38
axon 82, 109
azygos vein 146

B

back 16, 75
ball-and-socket joint 59
basilar artery 136
basilic vein 146
biceps brachii 62
biceps femoris 64
big toe/hallux 14
blood, components of 34
blood cells 27
body
  anatomical planes 18, 19
  anterior view 15
  cavities 16
  major arteries 135
  major veins 147
  overview 12–13
  posterior view 17
  regions 14–17
  symmetry and situs inversus 19
  view orientation 18
bone formation 53
bone tissue 20
Bowman's gland (olfactory gland) 109
brachial artery 134
brachial plexus 80, 170
brachial vein 146
brachialis 62
brachiocephalic artery (trunk) 122
brachiocephalic vein 122, 146, 170
brachioradialis 62
brain 90–103
  arteries 136–139
  functional areas 97, 98
  lateral view 91
  lobes 93, 98
  sagittal view 91
brainstem 90, 104
Broca's area (motor speech) 92
bronchi
  bronchial tree 177
  cross-section 175, 177
  lobar 160
  primary 160
  in situ 176
bronchial tree 177
buttock/gluteus 16

C

calcaneus 42
calcarine branch 136
calf/sura 16
callosomarginal artery 136
cancer, causes 29
capillaries 157
capillary bed 156

carcinoma of the larynx 162
cardiac branch of vagus nerve 170
cardiac muscle 21
carotid artery 122, 134, 136, 170
carpal bones 40
cartilage tissue 21
cataract 111
cauda equina 80
cell structure 24, 26
central canal 82
cephalic vein 146
cerebellar artery 136
cerebellum 90
cerebral aneurysms 139
cerebral artery 136
cerebral cortex 95
cerebrospinal fluid 101
cerebrum 90
cervical enlargement of spinal cord 80
cervical nerve 80
cervical vertebrae 38, 55
cheek (buccal) 14
chest/thorax (thoracic) 14
chin (mental) 14
chordae tendineae 122
choroid 106
cilia 109
cilia function, defects in 23
ciliary body 106
ciliary muscle 106
Circle of Willis 136, 137
circulatory system 12, 152
clavicles 38
coccyx 38
cochlea 107, 119
cochlear duct 107
cochlear nerve 107
cochlear (round) window 107
collagen 20
common carotid artery 122, 134, 136, 170
common fibular nerve 80
common iliac artery 134
common iliac vein 146
communicating artery 136
components of blood 34
connective tissue 20
coracoid process 40
cornea 106
coronary sinus 122
corpus callosum 90
corti 117
corticospinal tract 82
costal cartilage 38
costodiaphragmatic recess 170
cranial cavity 16

cribriform plate of ethmoid bone 109
cricoid cartilage 170
cricothyroid muscle 170
cuneate fasciculus 82

D

deep fibular nerve 80
deep muscles of the head 74
deep muscles of the neck 74
deep vein thrombosis 149
deltoid 60, 62
dense connective tissue 20
depressor anguli oris 60
descending aorta 122, 134
diaphragm 16, 160, 170, 183
digestive system 13
digital nerve 80
digits/fingers (digital or phalangeal) 14
distal orientation 18
dorsal arch 134
dorsal branch to corpus callosum 136
dorsal cavity 16
dorsal funiculus 82
dorsal horn 82
dorsal orientation 18
dorsal rootlets 82
dorsal spinocerebellar tract 82
dorsal surface 18
dorsal venous arch 146
dorsolateral sulcus 82
dura mater 82

E

ear 14, 107, 114
elastic cartilage 21
elbow (antecubital) 14
elbow/olecranon 16
ellipsoidal joint 57
endocrine system 13
endoneurium 82
epiglottis 108, 169
epilepsy 102
epineurium 82
epithelial tissue 20
eustachian (auditory) tube 107
extensor digitorum 62
extensor digitorum longus 64
extensor pollicis brevis 62
extensor retinaculum 62, 64
external abdominal oblique 60
external ear canal (meatus) 107
external iliac artery 134
external iliac vein 146
eye 14, 106

F

face 14, 96, 134
facial artery 134
facial nerve branches 96
false ribs (pairs 8–10) 38
female pelvis 45
femoral artery 134
femoral head 42, 48
femoral neck 42, 45
femoral nerve 80
femoral vein 146
femur 42, 43
fenestrated capillary 157
fibrocartilage 21
fibrous flexor sheath 62
fibula 42, 43
fibular artery 134
fibular nerve 80
fibular notch 42
fibularis (peroneus) longus 64
fila olfactoria 109
filiform papillae 108
fingers/digits (digital or
    phalangeal) 14
first rib 170
flexor carpi ulnaris 62
flexor digitorum superficialis 62
flexor retinaculum 62
floating ribs (pairs 11 & 12) 38
foot/pes (pedal) 14
forearm/antebrachium 14
forehead (frontal) 14
fornix 90
fovea capitis 42
fractured neck of femur 45
frontal bone 38
frontal (coronal) plane 18
frontal lobe 92, 109
frontalis 60
functional areas of brain 97, 98
functional cortical area 93
fungiform papillae 108

G

galea aponeurotica 60
gas exchange 181
gastrocnemius 64
glenoid cavity 40
glenoid fossa 40
gliding (plane) joint 56
glioma 95
gluteus maximus 64
gluteus medius 64
gracile fasciculus 82
gracilis 64
great saphenous vein 146
greater trochanter 42
greater tubercle of humerus 40
grey ramus communicans 82

groin/inguen (inguinal) 14
gyrus 90, 92

H

hair 30
hallux 14
hand 14, 51, 66
head 14
    deep muscles 74
    superficial arteries 153
    superficial muscles 61
    superficial veins 153
    surface arteries 139
head of femur 42, 48
head of fibula 42
head of humerus 40
heart 122–133, 134
    anterior view 131, 179
    cross-section 123
    cross-sectional view 130
heart valves 124–125
heartbeat 132
heel/calcaneus (calcaneal) 16
helicotrema 107
hinge joint 59
humerus 38, 40
hyaline tissue 21
hypothalamus 90, 103
hypothenar muscles 62

I

iliac artery 134
iliac crest 60
iliac vein 146
iliopsoas 64
iliotibial tract 64
ilium 38
immune system tissue 21
incus 107
inferior articular surface 42
inferior extensor retinaculum 64
inferior orientation 18
inferior pulmonary vein 122
inferior thyroid vein 170
inferior vena cava 122, 146
inguinal ligament 64
insula cortex 90
intercondylar eminence 42
intercondylar fossa 42
intercostal arteries 134
intercostal muscles 183
intercostal nerve 80
internal carotid artery 136
internal iliac artery 134
internal iliac vein 146
internal jugular vein 146, 170
internal thoracic vein 170
interosseous border 42

J

joints 40–46, 56–59
jugular vein 146, 170

K

kneecap/patella (patellar) 14

L

labyrinthine artery 136
lacrimal apparatus 166
larynx 160, 162, 163, 168
lateraal reticulospinal tract 82
lateral border of scapula 40
lateral condyle 42
lateral corticospinal tract 82
lateral epicondyle 42
lateral femoral cutaneous nerve 80
lateral fissure 92
lateral funiculus 82
lateral head of gastrocnemius 64
lateral head of triceps brachii 62
lateral malleolus 42
lateral orientation 18
lateral surface 42
lateral vestibulospinal tract 82
latissimus dorsi 60
leaflet/cusp of mitral valve
    122, 124
leaflet/cusp of tricuspid valve
    122, 124
left atrium 122, 124
left brachiocephalic vein 122, 170
left common carotid artery 122
left inferior pulmonary vein 122
left lower limb 43
left primary bronchus 160
left pulmonary artery 122
left subclavian artery 122
left superior pulmonary vein 122
left upper limb 41
left ventricle 122, 124
leg/crus (crural) 14
lens 106
lesser trochanter 42
lesser tubercle 40
levator labii superioris 60
limbic system, and smell 113
lingual tonsil 108
lobar bronchi 160
lobes of the brain 93, 98
long head of triceps brachii 62
loose connective tissue 20
lower back (lumbar) 16
lower limb 16
    arteries 144
    bones and joints 42–43
    major nerves 89
    muscles 64–65
    veins 148

lower lobar bronchus 160
lower lobes (left/right lung) 170
lower teeth 38
lumbar vertebra 38, 55
lumbosacral enlargement of spinal
    cord 80
lumbosacral plexus 80
lung disease 77
lungs 77, 131, 170–171, 179
lymph node 22
lymphatic system 12

M

major arteries of the body 135
major nerves of lower limb 89
major nerves of upper limb 88
major veins of the body 147
malleus 107
mandible 38
masseter 60
maxilla 38
medial border of scapula 40
medial condyle 42
medial epicondyle 42
medial frontal branches 136
medial frontobasal artery 136
medial malleolus 42
medial occipital artery 136
medial orientation 18
medial reticulospinal tract 82
medial striate artery 136
medial vestibulospinal tract 82
median antebrachial vein 146
median nerve 80
median plane 18
median sulcus 108
mediastinum 16
medulla oblongata 80
Ménière's disease 117
metacarpal bone 40
metatarsal bones 42
mid-sagittal plane 18
middle cerebral artery 136
middle lobar bronchus 160
middle lobe (right lung) 170
mitochondrial disease 25
mitral cell 109
mitral valve 122, 124, 125
motor speech area (Broca's) 92
mouth (oral) 14
muscle(s)
    fibre 68
    of the hand 66
    of lung disease 77
    muscular system 12
    of the neck 76
    shapes 69
    tissue 21
    of ventilation 77

muscular system 12
musculocutaneous nerve 80
myelin sheath of Schwann cell 82
myocardial infarction 127

N
nail 30
nasal cavity 160
nasal (piriform) aperture 38
neck (cervical) 14
    muscles 61, 74, 76
    superficial arteries 153
    superficial veins 153
    surface arteries 139
neck of femur 42, 45
neck of fibula 42
nervous system 12, 81
neural tissue 20
neuron 26, 85
node of ranvier 82
normal vein, structure 150
nose 14, 115

O
obturator artery 134
obturator nerve 80
occipital bone 38
occipital lobe 92
occipitalis 60
olfactory apparatus 109
olfactory bulb 109
olfactory gland (Bowman's
    gland) 109
olfactory mucosa 109
olfactory nerve cell 109
olfactory system 115
olfactory tract 109
opening of coronary sinus 122
optic nerve 106
orbicularis oculi 60
orbicularis oris 60
orbit 38
organ of Corti 117
ossicles 107
osteogenesis imperfecta 33

P
painful arc syndrome 71
palatine tonsil 108
palatoglossus muscle and
    arch 108
palatopharyngeus muscle and
    arch 108
palm (palmar) 14
palmar arterial arches 134
palmar surface 18
palmar venous arch 146
palmaris brevis 62
palmaris longus 62

papillary muscle 122
para-median plane 18
para-sagittal plane 18
paracentral artery 136
paranasal sinuses 164, 166
paraplegia 86, 87
parietal bone 38
parietal lobe 92
parietooccipital branch 136
patella 42
patellar surface 42
pectineus 64
pectoralis major 60, 62, 170
pelvic cavity 16
pelvic floor muscles (female) 73
pelvic wall, arteries 143
pelvis 14, 45
pericallosal artery 136
pericardial cavity 16
pericardium 122, 170
perineurium 82
peripheral nervous system 80–81
phalanges 40, 42
pharynx 160, 167
pia mater 82
pineal gland 90
piriform aperture 38
pivot joint 58
plantar arch 134
plantar surface 18
plantar venous arch 146
pneumonia 172
pneumothorax 175
polar frontal artery 136
pollex 14
popliteal archery 134
portal system 142
postcentral gyrus 92
posterior auricular artery 134
posterior cerebral artery 136
posterior chamber 106
posterior communicating
    artery 136
posterior inferior cerebellar
    artery 136
posterior orientation 18
posterior ramus of spinal
    nerve 82
posterior spinal artery 82
posterior spinal vein 82
posterior tibial artery 134
precentral gyrus (motor
    cortex) 92
precuneal artery 136
prefrontal cortex 92
primary auditory cortex 92
primary bronchi 160
primary motor cortex 92
primary somatosensory cortex 92

primary visual cortex 92
promontary covering first coil of
    cochlea 107
pronator teres 62
proximal orientation 18
pubis (pubic) 14
pulmonary artery 122, 129
pulmonary circulation 127
pulmonary valve 122, 124
pulmonary vein 122

R
radial artery 134
radial nerve 80
radicular artery 82
radius 40
ramus of spinal nerve 82
reading comprehension area 92
rectus abdominis 60
renal artery 134, 143
renal vein 146
reproductive system 13
respiratory muscles 183
respiratory system 13, 160–169
    anterior view 161, 182
    diaphragm 183
    intercostal muscles 183
    upper part 161, 183
retina 106, 110
rheumatic heart disease 128
ribs
    false (pairs 8–10) 38
    first 170
    floating (pairs 11 & 12) 38
    true (pairs 1–7) 38
right anterior cerebral artery 136
right atrium 122, 124, 170
right brachiocephalic vein 122,
    170
right inferior pulmonary vein 122
right lower limb 43
right primary bronchus 160
right pulmonary artery 122
right upper limb 41
right ventricle 122, 124, 170
rotator cuff and painful arc
    syndrome 71
rotator cuff muscles 71

S
saccular macula 107
saccule 107
sacrum 38
saddle joint 56
sagittal fissure 90
sagittal (mid-sagittal or median)
    plane 18
sagittal (para-sagittal or para-
    median) plane 18

sagittal plane 18
saphenous vein, small 146
scalenus anterior 170
scalp 30
scapula 38, 40
Schwann cell, myelin sheath 82
sciatic nerve 80
semicircular canals 107
semimembranosus 64
semitendinosus 64
sensory speech area
    (Wernicke's) 92
serratus anterior 60
shaft (diaphysis) of femur 42
shoulder (acromial) 16
    cross-section 46
    dislocation 47
    joint 40, 41
shoulder joint 40, 41
sinusitis 165
situs inversus 19
skeletal muscle 21
skeletal system 12
skin 12, 30, 33
skull/cranium (cranial) 14, 49
small saphenous vein 146
smell and the limbic system 113
smooth muscle 21
sole (plantar) 16
soleus 64
somatosensory association
    area 92
spinal anaesthesia 105
spinal artery 82
spinal canal 16
spinal cord 82–83, 90
    anterior view 105
    cervical enlargement of 80
    cross-sectional view 83
    lumbosacral enlargement of 80
spinal (dorsal root) ganglion 83
spinal grey matter 83
spinal nerves 105
spinal vein 82
spine of scapula 40
spinothalamic tract 83
spinous processes 38
stapes 107
stapes footplate covering
    vestibular (oval) window 107
sternocleidomastoid 60
sternohyoid 60
sternum 38
structure of a normal vein 150
subclavian artery 122, 134, 170
subclavian vein 146, 170
subscapular fossa 40
sulcus 90, 92

superficial arteries of the head
    and neck 153
superficial fibular nerve 80
superficial muscles of the
    back 75
superficial muscles of the
    head 61
superficial muscles of the
    lower limb 65
superficial muscles of the
    neck 61
superficial muscles of the
    trunk 61
superficial muscles of the
    upper limb 63
superficial veins of the head
    and neck 153
superior articular surfaces (medial
    and lateral facets) 42
superior border of scapula 40
superior cerebellar artery 136
superior extensor retinaculum 64
superior lobar bronchus 160
superior orientation 18
superior pulmonary vein 122
superior vena cava 122, 146, 170
sural nerve 80
surface arteries of the head and
    neck 139
suspensory ligaments 106
sweat gland 28

T
talus 42
tarsal bones 42
temporal bone 38
temporal lobe 92
temporalis 60
tendon of flexor carpi ulnaris 62
tendon of palmaris longus 62
tendon of triceps brachii 62
tendons of extensors of the
    digits 62
teres major 60
teres minor 60
terminal sulcus 108
thalamus 90
thenar muscles 62
thigh (femoral) 14
thigh muscle injury 67
thoracic cavity 16
thoracic vein 170
thoracic vertebra 38, 55
thoracolumbar fascia 60
thumb/pollex (pollical) 14
thymus 170
thyroid gland 170
tibia 42, 43
tibial artery 134

tibial nerve 80
tibial tuberosity 42
tibialis anterior 64
tissues 20–21
toes/digits (digital or
    phalangeal) 14
tongue 108, 112
torso 14, 61
trachea 160, 170
    cross-section 172, 177
    in situ 176
transverse (axial) plane 18
transverse processes 38
trapezius 60
traumatic neck injury 50
triceps brachii 60, 62
tricuspid valve 122, 124, 125
true ribs (pairs 1–7) 38
trunk/torso 14, 61
tympanic duct 107
tympanic membrane
    (eardrum) 107

U
ulna 40
ulnar artery 134
ulnar nerve 80
umbilicus (umbilical) 14
upper limb 16
    arteries 141
    bones and joints 40–41
    major nerves 88
    muscles 62–63
    veins 154
upper lobar bronchus 160
upper lobe (left/right lungs) 170
upper part of the respiratory
    system 161, 183
upper teeth 38
urinary system 13
utricle 107

V
vagus nerve, cardiac branch 170
vallate papillae 108
vallecula 108
varicose veins 150
veins 146–147
    head and neck 153
    lower limb 148
    major 147
    structure 150
    upper limb 154
    varicose 150
venous stasis ulcers 155
ventilation, muscles of 77
ventral funiculus 83
ventral horn 83
ventral rootlets 83

ventral spinocerebellar tract 83
ventricle 122, 124, 170
ventricular diastole 124
ventricular systole 124
vertebral artery 136
vertebral column 54
vestibular duct 107
vestibular nerve branches 107
view orientation 18
visual association area 92
vitreous body 106

W
white ramus communications 83
wrist (carpal) 14, 40, 88

Z
zygomatic bone 38
zygomaticus major 60